THE ROMANCE
OF
EXPLORATION
AND
EMERGENCY FIRST-AID
FROM
STANLEY TO BYRD

SECTIONAL INDEX

TRADE MARK

BURROUGHS WELLCOME & CO. (U.S.A.) (INC.)
9–11 & 13–15, EAST 41ST STREET
NEW YORK CITY

Associated Houses:

LONDON   MONTREAL   SYDNEY   CAPE TOWN   MILAN

BOMBAY   SHANGHAI   BUENOS AIRES

A

SIR H. M. STANLEY—FIRST TO CROSS DARKEST AFRICA

Sir H. M. Stanley and his porters being attacked by pygmies in the forest jungles of Equatorial Africa

THE ROMANCE OF EXPLORATION

AND EMERGENCY FIRST-AID

FROM

STANLEY TO BYRD

INTRODUCTION

CURIOSITY AND PROGRESS

> "I have six honest serving men
> They serve me till I die.
> Their names are who and what and when
> and how and where and why."

So says Rudyard Kipling in praise of the much under-estimated virtue of curiosity. The Turks have an ancient proverb which should be remembered in this connexion: "The world belongs to the dissatisfied." It is to the curiosity and dissatisfaction of great and indomitable souls that we owe all human progress.

There is no chapter in man's advancement more dramatic and more valuable than the history of exploration. To satisfy their curiosity, heroic souls have gone to the ends of the earth. For this, they have given their strength, frequently their health and their lives. They have dared everything to penetrate the mysteries of the unknown. They have braved the terrific colds and blasts of the Arctic and Antarctic. They have trudged their way through the torrid, disease-ridden jungles of the Tropics. They have taken their chances on uncharted seas. Maps of a hundred years ago contained vast areas that were marked "unexplored" or "unknown" territory. To-day there are comparatively few parts of the earth that can be so described.

The curiosity of heroic souls

ADMIRAL PEARY—FIRST TO REACH THE NORTH POLE

Admiral Robert E. Peary and five companions grouped on a hard Snow Mound erected at the North Pole, April 6, 1909

This progress does not mean just a difference in our maps, an increased bulkiness in our text-books of geography; it means also a prodigious growth in the sum of all human knowledge. The great explorers have contributed to all the **Explorers contribute to all sciences** sciences, whether intentionally or otherwise. They have caused the sphere of medical science to expand. They have contributed to the speed and ease with which we now move from one place to another. They have even added to our everyday comfort.

For instance, early in the 18th century, the Sieur Charles Marie de la Condamine went to Peru to measure the meridian. He also explored the Amazon and brought back to civilisation the idea for making practical use of rubber. Thanks to him, we now travel along the highways in our cars or other vehicles with consummate comfort.

There are many things which we look upon as a matter of course which we owe to the curiosity of explorers. In medicine, for instance, there is quinine derived from cinchona bark originally brought by pioneers from South America. Strophanthus, nux vomica and other valuable medicines have been made available by the exploration of Africa, Asia and other parts of the world. But for the travels of Livingstone, Burton, Speke, Stanley and others in Africa, of Captain Cook and others to the South Sea Islands, soap would not be so cheap and easy to procure as it is to-day.

Such a list, as can readily be imagined, is endless. Many of the most invaluable discoveries came as by-products of an explorer's achievement. Martin Frobisher, the great Elizabethan mariner, did not go looking for the North-West Passage in order to found the whaling industry. H. M. Stanley did not plunge into Darkest Africa for the sake of making palm oil available to soap makers. When Robert E. Peary went to the **Invaluable discoveries** North Pole, he had not the faintest idea that people would eventually be making use of his discoveries to endeavour to establish a safe transatlantic route for aeroplanes. An entire volume, in fact, could be written about the contributions to progress, which were indirect outcomes of an explorer's labours and fortitude.

SIR JOHN ALCOCK—FIRST TO MAKE DIRECT TRANSATLANTIC FLIGHT

Sir John Alcock's Machine approaching the Irish Coast on the morning of June 15, 1919

Indeed, America itself is a case in point. To its earliest discoverers this Continent was a nuisance. From Columbus to Hudson they would have been only too glad to give it away, to push it on one side— anything to have it out of the way. It was actually a bitter disappointment to Columbus that the West Indies were not the East Indies. He had very little use for the land he had found. When Henry Hudson discovered the river and the great northern bay that bear his name, he was not particularly elated. He, like Columbus and all the other earliest adventurers to the Americas, wanted a quick road to far Cathay, to China and the wealth of the Indies. Even the fact that they brought back to Europe the tobacco plant, the potato, the tomato and the turkey was considered inadequate compensation for their failure to find the short-cut to India.

SCIENCE AND EXPLORATION

To-day we are able to form a clearer picture of what the explorers in the past have achieved and what those of the present are achieving ; and it is stimulating to reflect that, if the explorers have contributed to the advancement of science, science to-day is contributing vastly to the well-being of the explorers. The earlier pages of the history of this domain of human endeavour are darkly studded with tragedy. Not merely the tragedy of failure, but of complete disaster, such as happened to the expeditions of Mungo Park to the source of the Niger in Africa and of Sir John Franklin to the Arctic.

A danger far worse than that of broken limbs, of cuts and gun-shot wounds, hangs over the traveller in remote places, particularly in the Tropics. The worst menace he has to face is disease. In those regions a mere scratch on a finger can produce an immediate infection. Up to a comparatively The menace short time ago, the only effective antiseptic known of disease to man in such a case was cauterisation. To be sure of cleaning a wound, it was necessary to burn it with a red-hot iron. The same red-hot iron was the only means of preventing gangrene after an operation. Until the middle of the last century there was no such

U.S.A. ARMY AIRMEN—FIRST TO FLY ROUND THE WORLD

Landing at Croydon, England, before the penultimate stage of their world flight

thing as a really effective general or local anæsthetic, though some ancient writers mention the fact that Indian hemp, either smoked or eaten, was used in parts of Asia. But the master of a vessel in the day of Sir John Franklin or Sir William Edward Parry, if he had to perform an amputation on any of his crew, could do nothing to dull the patient's pain but give him a good stiff tot of rum.

The Tropics, as we have observed, are by far the most dangerous regions for travellers. There, in addition to the ever-dangerous scurvy, they encounter such desolating ailments as black fever, yellow fever, dysentery, typhoid, sleeping-sickness, beri-beri and the ever-present smallpox. All of these are particularly fatal to the so-called white man, that is the man who originates in the temperate zones. In addition, there is malaria, which, although it occurs in temperate climates, is much more prevalent and virulent in the Tropics. In some of these far-off places, the natives have a degree of immunity to certain diseases. But that immunity is not enjoyed by invaders from the temperate zones. The ravages from these diseases up to some 50 years ago, as we shall presently see, were terrific.

MEDICAL EQUIPMENT

The earlier explorer went out into the jungle equipped with little more than a small quantity of quinine, castor oil and perhaps a few rolls of bandage. He often found that any other drugs he took with him were soon useless, because they deteriorated so rapidly in hot climates; or else they were so bulky that it was impossible to carry them through thousands of miles Crude of tropic jungle. So he had to take his chances. equipment of early When H. M. Stanley came back after he had found travellers Dr. Livingstone, he said: "When I think of the dreadful mortality of Capt. Tuckey's Expedition in 1816, of the Niger Expedition in 1841, of the sufferings of Burton and Speke, and of my own first expeditions, I am amazed to find that much of the mortality and sickness was due to the crude way in which medicines were supplied to travellers. The very recollection causes me to shudder."

REAR-ADMIRAL BYRD—TRANSATLANTIC FLIGHT AMERICA TO FRANCE

Rear-Admiral Byrd, the only airman to fly to the North and South Poles, interposed between these achievements a flight from America to France

In the Arctic and Antarctic regions there are not, to be sure, so many dangers of disease. Infection is practically unknown. There is no such thing in the frigid zones as malaria, yellow fever, beri-beri, sleeping sickness. There are no such things as head colds, bronchitis or pneumonia. The two greatest perils for Arctic explorers—other than death from freezing—are starvation and scurvy. It seems difficult to realise now that it was not until the expedition of Sir William Parry in the "Hecla" in 1819 that there was any mention of an expedition carrying medical equipment. Even Parry had no means of warding off scurvy. The experiences of all the early explorers show that scurvy was due to a lack of fresh food. Without fresh game or vegetables, travellers depended upon a diet of salt beef. It is now known that scurvy is caused by a lack of Vitamin C. Thanks to modern pharmacy, this Vitamin C can be supplied as a compressed product and be available to prevent scurvy when the supply of fresh vegetables is exhausted.

So one of the greatest steps forward made in a century of progress is our ability to equip the explorer of to-day, so that he can combat the perils of those deadly diseases. Before he leaves his home port he is inoculated against typhoid and typhus as well as smallpox. He takes with him in small compact **Modern medical equipments** packages, which can be easily and safely carried, a complete medical outfit. Medicaments, bandages and dressings are so compressed that an ample supply can be taken, and there is the surety that they will retain their efficiency indefinitely. The pioneer work in this domain has been done by Burroughs Wellcome & Company.

After H. M. Stanley returned from his hazardous exploits in Darkest Africa, he made, in his own words, "the acquaintance of Burroughs Wellcome & Co.," and his medical equipment problem was solved. This firm, impressed by the sufferings of early explorers, the lack of knowledge of tropical diseases and the impossibility of carrying adequate medical supplies, owing to the bulk of medicines hitherto available, had instituted scientific research into the causes and treatment of tropical ailments and had made special studies of the problem of medical supplies and equipments for travellers.

As a result, they were able, not only to supply compact medicine cases fitted with compressed medicaments which were impervious to climatic influences, but also to give intending travellers and explorers expert advice as to the character and quantities of the medicines they would need in accordance with the part of the world in which they proposed to travel, and the diseases by which they would be liable to be attacked.

Stanley was one of the first to avail himself of the results of this specialised research. In his later expeditions, he was always equipped with 'Tabloid' Medical Outfits, and since that time Burroughs Wellcome & Co. have supplied the medical equipments of practically every important expedition.

'Tabloid' Medicine Chests and Cases and 'Tabloid' First-Aid Outfits have become the standard equipments for travellers. They have accompanied the pioneers of tropical exploration through the jungles of Equatorial Africa, Asia and South America, as well as travellers to unknown parts of the temperate zones; they have played so prominent a part in Arctic and Antarctic discovery that they are the only medical outfits to have been carried to the North or to the South Pole; they have supplied the needs of the great pioneer aviators during their epoch-making flights.

The experiences of these brilliant adventurers have shown that 'Tabloid' equipments meet every need, not only because they take up so little room, but for the far more important reason that they are immune to the effects of any climate and to any weather conditions. Their 'Tabloid' contents remain as active at the end of years as on the day they were first acquired.

In the following pages we shall consider briefly the stories of some of these historic expeditions; and we shall trace, by contrasting histories, the progress that has been made in the century.

The original equipments form a highly interesting collection of historic value and are displayed at the Burroughs Wellcome & Co. Exhibit in the Hall of Science at the Chicago Century of Progress Exposition, 1934. At the conclusion of the Exposition, the entire collection of exhibits will be transferred to the firm's permanent Exhibition Galleries at Nos. 9–11 & 13–15, East Forty-first Street, New York City.

PIONEER HEROES OF AFRICA

UNTIL the 18th century, Africa was, so far as white men were concerned, the great unknown Continent. Exploration of the interior was confined practically to Arab adventurers, traders for the most part, of whose journeys we know little. The modern epoch of African exploration begins with a Scot—James Bruce—who, from 1768–1772, spent an adventurous life in **James Bruce** Abyssinia and Northern Africa. He traced the Blue Nile to its source, and, in spite of almost indescribable hardship, particularly in the Nubian Desert, returned to record his discoveries. He was almost the only one of his expedition to survive.

THE NIGER

In 1788, there was founded the African Association for the Promotion of Exploration. Its early attention was directed mainly to the Niger, of which neither source nor mouth was known. Disease and murder accounted for the lives of several explorers.

One of the outstanding tragedies was that of Mungo Park; and his experience becomes all the more significant because he was a surgeon by training. In 1795, Dr. Mungo Park got as far as the Gambia. He went up the river 200 miles to a British trading station and thence plunged into the unknown. By extraordinary efforts he crossed the upper Senegal Basin. **Mungo Park** Wandering through the desert regions, he was captured and kept prisoner for months by a Moorish chieftain. He escaped with difficulty, reached the Niger on July 20, 1796, and followed its course until he was seized by bandits and robbed of practically everything he possessed. He was protected by a dealer, who made Mungo Park his guest until he recovered from the fever which had seized him. He then accompanied the caravan for 500 miles, finally reaching Gambia in safety.

SIR HENRY MORTON STANLEY, G.C.B., D.C.L., LL.D., PH.D.

One of SIR H. M. STANLEY'S 'TABLOID' MEDICINE CHESTS

His experiences on that journey would have been enough for half-a-dozen ordinary men. But, in 1805, Mungo Park again responded to the call of Africa. He sailed from Portsmouth in January, 1805. When he reached the banks of the Niger, in the middle of August, only 11 Europeans of his party were alive. He employed the next few weeks reorganising his expedition. Out of two canoes, he built one long boat. In this he set off down the river. From that day nothing more was seen of him by white men. It was subsequently inferred that Mungo Park and his party had reached the Bussa Rapids and had there been drowned or massacred.

In 1823, Denham reached Lake Tchad. In 1823, Clapperton and Lander arrived at Lagos and followed the Niger to Bussa and gathered news of Dr. Mungo Park's end. They reached Sokoto, where Clapperton died. Lander returned and undertook a second Niger Expedition— 1830—which resulted in the discovery and penetration of the Niger delta. Lander was awarded the first Royal Premium by the Royal Geographical Society which had been founded in the year of his return.

Other Niger pioneers

THE NILE

It was not until the latter half of the century that the main source of the Nile was definitely established as being Lake Victoria Nyanza. Nobody knows how many people died to add this fact to the world's knowledge. Others went through sufferings uncountable. The discovery came about through the combined efforts of Sir Richard Francis Burton and Captain John Hanning Speke. Of the two, Burton was by far the more colourful. His most sensational feat was to penetrate, disguised as a Mohammedan, to Medineh and Mecca, in the holy places of Islam. In 1856, the Royal Geographical Society sent him and Speke to explore Africa's great equatorial lakes, Tanganyika, Victoria Nyanza and Albert Nyanza. It is a matter of record that when they reached the shores of Tanganyika, both Speke and Burton were so weak from fever that they could scarcely sit in their saddles. When they arrived, Speke fainted, and they were the only white men in their party who had survived.

Burton and Speke

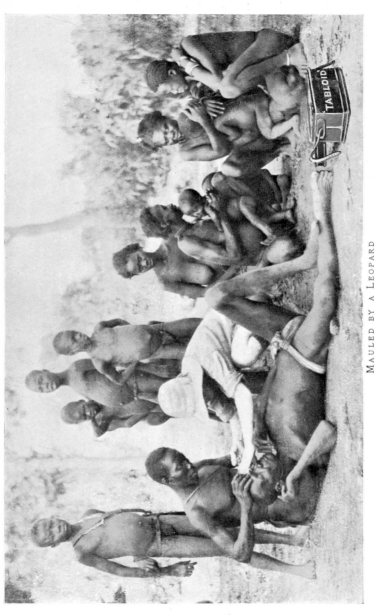

MAULED BY A LEOPARD

An African Chief, badly mauled by a leopard, receiving treatment at the hands of Mrs. Glover, wife of Mr. T. A. Glover, leader of the "Glover Expedition to Tibesti"

Speke had his own ideas as to the source of the Nile. Burton did not agree with him. While Burton lay ill, Speke made a preliminary survey of Victoria Nyanza. He obtained proof that the great river had its origin there. Later on, with a Scottish explorer named James A. Grant, he followed the course of the Nile, thus definitely confirming his theory.

During this journey in 1863, Speke and Grant met another famous African explorer, Samuel Baker, who was ascending the Nile in search of them. Speke informed Baker of the existence of another great lake to the west of **Baker** Unyoro. Baker decided to take up the quest for this, and, as a result, he discovered Albert Nyanza in 1864. Then he proceeded up the Victoria Nile and discovered the Murchison Falls.

In spite of this, the mystery of the source of the Nile was not finally elucidated until Livingstone's theory, that it had its origin in Tanganyika, was disposed of by the joint survey of this lake by Livingstone and Stanley, and until Stanley, during his last two great journeys, completely established the fact that, while the chief source was Victoria Nyanza, there were also lakes Albert Edward and Albert, connected by the Semliki River. These lakes derived their supplies from tropical rain and the snow-fields of the Mountains of the Moon. Further reference to this matter will be found in the notes on Stanley on *pages* 20–27.

LIVINGSTONE

Meanwhile, David Livingstone, the famous missionary whose name is inseverably associated with Africa, had been accumulating a vast fund of knowledge about the country to the amelioration of whose people's lot he devoted his life. Through the territory of the savage, hostile tribes he often travelled quite unarmed. The natives

RELIC 'TABLOID' MEDICINE CASES—AFRICA

1—Medicine Belt carried by Capt. Stairs throughout his Katanga Expedition. 2—The famous "Rear-Guard" Medicine Chest used during Sir H. M. Stanley's travels. 3—Extricated from the ruins after the Bandawe Mission House had been demolished by lightning; the contents that escaped damage were used for more than ten years afterwards. 4—Once the property of E. G. Glave. Supplied for a journey made concerning the great slave question of Central Africa. This Case was afterwards damaged in the Brussels Exhibition Fire, 1910.

5—Carried by Capt. Thomas Stevens on the Expedition in East Africa to find Stanley. 6—Chest carried by Sir H. M. Stanley during the Emin Pasha Relief and other Expeditions. 7—Formerly the property of Dr. Percy Rendall, Principal Medical Officer, British Central Africa Administration. 8—Case carried by Frank Muxworthy, the famous African Caravan Leader, on three journeys through Uganda. 9—The last Medicine Chest supplied to Emin Pasha. This Chest was also damaged in the Brussels Exhibition Fire, 1910.

everywhere, by common accord, called him "The Great Master."
His life was an epic of accomplishments in the face of bitter obstacles.
Livingstone went to work in a cotton factory at the age of 10 and kept
at that job for 14 years. When he became seized by the desire to become
a missionary, he realised that something more than
theology was needed. He qualified as a physician.   "The
Livingstone landed at Algoa Bay in 1841 and trekked   Great
to Kuruman in Bechuanaland, where was situated   Master"
the most inland station of the London Missionary Society and the
headquarters of Robert Moffat, who later surveyed the greater part
of the Orange River. Livingstone went northward unaccompanied by
any other white man. He discovered Lake Ngami. Subsequently
(1851), he discovered the Zambezi River and traced its course to its
mouth in the Indian Ocean (1856). Incidentally, he also discovered
the famous Victoria Falls. In 1859, Livingstone undertook an
important expedition which resulted in the creation of the Nyassaland
Protectorate.

The versatility and ability of the man were shown by the fact
that, with mostly native labour, he built a river steamer in which
he pursued his travels.

Returning to England, he obtained funds for another expedition.
Some of the money was furnished by the British Government, some
by the Royal Geographical Society, and some by private individuals.
This journey had a double purpose: first, to investigate and, if possible,
suppress the slave trade in Central Africa; second, to explore the
water sheds of Lakes Tanganyika and Nyassa. He organised his
expedition in Bombay. When he started (1866) he had 13 sepoys
and some 23 African natives. Before he had been in Africa many
months his staff was reduced to four or five native boys. This was
his last and most famous journey and the time of his severest
privations. Among other mishaps, his medicine chest was stolen.
That is why his men died, dropping off like flies.

For several years nothing was heard of him. The report
went throughout the civilised world that Livingstone was lost in
Darkest Africa.

STANLEY

It was at this point that the figure of Henry Morton Stanley entered into the picture. Born in Wales in 1840, he left England as a cabin boy on a ship sailing for New Orleans. Thus early, and later before the mast and in the United States Navy, he familiarised himself with navigating instruments and their use, which was of great service to him in his explorations. Then he was adopted by a cotton broker. However, the benevolent broker died without making provision for his adopted son. When the Civil War broke out, young Stanley volunteered for service, was taken prisoner and finally invalided out of the army owing to dysentery and fever.

Stanley first obtained experience as a journalist by acting as a newspaper correspondent during the Civil War, and, on its conclusion in 1865, definitely entered journalistic life. In 1867, he was delegated to accompany General Hancock in the Indian wars of the West and General Sherman on the Indian Peace Commission, and acquired outstanding ability and considerable reputation as a descriptive writer. He was engaged by *The New York Herald* and one of his first assignments was to accompany the British Expedition against the Emperor Theodore of Abyssinia in 1867–68. After that he was given a roving commission by James Gordon Bennett, the younger.

When the report went throughout the civilised world: "Dr. Livingstone is lost," Bennett sent for Stanley and said: "I want you to find Livingstone." Stanley gasped. Though he had no experience as an explorer, he had a sound idea of the organisation and expense that such an expedition would require. He said as much to Bennett, who replied: "Take what you want, but find Livingstone." However, Stanley first was given several other assignments in Egypt, Syria and Persia. So it was not until March, 1871, that he left Zanzibar, at the head of a considerable expedition and began a career which was to start a new chapter in the history of exploration.

Commission to find Livingstone

On November 10, 1871, he arrived at a place called Ujiji. There, he encountered a tall, white man with a grey beard, whom he approached with the historic words: "Dr. Livingstone, I presume."

Stanley spent from November 10, 1871, to March 14, 1872, with Livingstone. During this time they explored together the north end of Lake Tanganyika and disproved the theory that the lake had any connexion with Albert Nyanza or the Nile.

As the missionary declined to return to Europe, because he wished to continue the work he was doing in Africa, Stanley left him a new equipment and went back to Europe to give the world, not only the epic story of the finding of Livingstone, but a fund of invaluable geographical information which threw a new light on Central Africa. Livingstone died in Africa, two years later, of dysentery.

As correspondent of *The New York Herald*, Stanley next accompanied the British Expeditionary Force against the Ashantis in 1873-74.

In 1874, he set out on another pioneer African journey which was to become famous as "Through the Dark Continent." It was undertaken under the auspices of *The New York Herald* and *The Daily Telegraph* (London, Eng.). Its object was to "complete the work left unfinished by the lamentable death of Dr. Livingstone; to solve, if possible, the remaining problems of the geography of Central Africa." Stanley was announced as representing the two nations whose common interest was the regeneration of Africa.

"Through the Dark Continent"

In January, 1875, Stanley reached the Victoria Nyanza and spent over a year tracing the extreme southern sources of the Nile through marshy plains to this great reservoir. He circumnavigated the lake, exploring every inlet and creek. The stupendous nature of this task will be realised by the fact that Victoria Nyanza covers a superficial area of 21,500 square miles.

Stanley, after discovering Albert Edward Nyanza, proceeded to Lake Tanganyika, which he explored thoroughly, and, after a march of 220 miles, reached the Congo, on the banks of which Livingstone died. He followed the river down its course, and, in August, 1877, reached Boma, having cleared up the geographical uncertainties of the Nile and Congo left unsettled by Livingstone and Speke, and having accomplished one of the greatest of his African journeys.

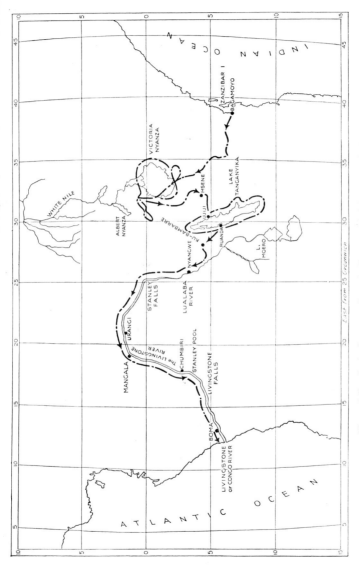

Map of Stanley's Journey through Equatorial Africa, 1874–77

During his return from the Expedition, Stanley, in his letters to the Press, stated his plan to pour the civilisation of Europe into the barbarism of Africa by linking up the waterway of the Upper Congo with the coast. The plan did not commend itself to the English Government, but aroused the enthusiasm of King Leopold of Belgium. Finally, in January, 1879, Stanley accepted the leadership of an Expedition on behalf of the "Comité d'Etude du Haut Congo."

Starting from the mouth of the Congo on August 15, 1879, Stanley worked up the course of the river, by water where possible and then overland, establishing stations as he went and making treaties with the natives. From Stanley Pool, where free navigation of the Upper Congo begins, it extends **The Congo Free State** for 1070 miles to Stanley Falls. He established the station of Leopoldville in honour of the King of the Belgians. Disabled by fever, he returned to England in 1882 and reported to the "Comité de l'Association Internationale du Congo," which had now been formed. In six weeks he was on his way back. For 18 months he negotiated further treaties, dealing with over 400 chiefs ; and so the foundations of the Congo Free State were established.

During one of the brief intervals between his great journeys, Stanley spoke of the difficulties encountered by explorers in combating disease and made the statement, already quoted on *page* 9 :—

> "When I think of the dreadful mortality of Capt. Tuckey's Expedition in 1816, of the Niger Expedition of 1841, of the sufferings of Burton and Speke, and of my own first expeditions, I am amazed to find that much of the mortality and sickness was due to the crude way in which medicines were supplied to travellers. The very recollection causes me to shudder."

It was left to Burroughs Wellcome & Co. to remedy this state of things. Their research work and intense study of the medical requirements of explorers and travellers, of tropical diseases and their treatment, and of the best methods of presenting and carrying efficient medicines, had resulted in the revolution of medical equipments. Special investigations were made into conditions occurring in different fields of operations and in regard to diseases prevalent

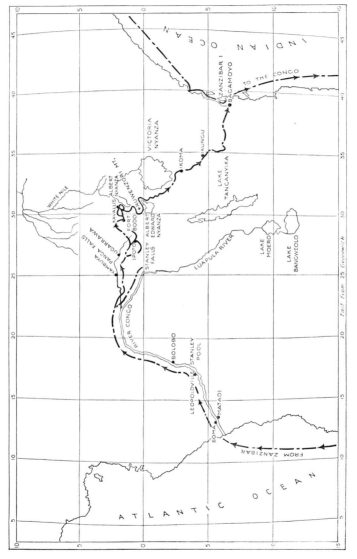

Map of the Route of the Emin Pasha Relief Expedition, 1887-89

in various territories visited by venturesome explorers. By these means, a great store of accumulated knowledge and experience was available to be placed at the disposal of travellers, and their medical equipments were fitted with supplies suitable to the countries which they proposed to explore or visit.

As Stanley himself said :—

"I made the acquaintance of Messrs. Burroughs Wellcome & Co. As soon as I came in sight of their preparations and their work, I found the consummation of my secret wish. On my later expeditions I had all the medicines that were required for my black men, as well as my white men, beautifully prepared, and in most elegant fashion arranged in the smallest medicine chest it was ever my lot to carry into Africa."

Stanley's last expedition was in search of another European in peril in Africa. This man was a combination of scientist, adventurer, traveller and administrator, and was known as Emin Pasha. He was a German, whose real name was Edouard Schnitzer. Trained first as a doctor, he became interested in natural history, zoology and ornithology, and acquired quite a name as a collector. He went to Turkey and obtained employ-

Emin Pasha

ment in the Quarantine Service of the Turkish Government. After holding several positions, he was sent to Khartoum as medical officer to General Gordon. The hero of Khartoum not only employed him as a physician, but sent him out on important political missions. In 1878, Emin was appointed Governor of the Equatorial Province. He was subsequently given the title of Pasha.

He administered his province successfully until the ferocious fanatical Mahdist uprising of 1882. He was cut off, by the wild hordes of insurgents under the leadership of the Khalifa, from contact with the Sudan administration at Khartoum, where his chief, General Gordon, carried on his heroic defence of the city and the native population until the overwhelming catastrophe of his death on January 26, 1885, the massacre of his garrison and the reduction of the population to slavery and the Sudan to barbarism.

During this terrible period the people were also stricken with tropical diseases, and the population of the Sudan reduced, according to Slatin Pasha's estimate, by 12 to 15 millions, of whom 8 to 10 millions died of disease and famine.

Stanley went to the rescue of Emin. He arrived at Matadi on March 21, 1887, and pushed through the great Equatorial forest in an effort to reach Emin, who was presumed to be in the neighbourhood of Albert Nyanza, about 1800 miles away. In April, 1888, Stanley found Emin on the shores of the lake. They spent several months together, but Emin declined to return beyond Zanzibar. Emin subsequently entered the service of the German Government and headed an expedition to Lakes Victoria and Albert. There was mutiny among his men, and, in 1892, he was murdered.

Among the effects of Emin Pasha that were subsequently recovered was a letter to Burroughs Wellcome & Co., in which he wrote :—

"I found the medicine chest you forwarded me fully stocked. I need not tell you that its very completeness made bound my heart. Articles like those could not be made but at the hands of the greatest artists in their own departments. If anyone relieved from intense pain pours out his blessings, they will come home to you.

"I should like to expatiate somewhat longer on the intrinsical value, but sickness preventing me to do so, I wish you to believe me."

Dr. Emin Pasha

(DR. EMIN PASHA)

The 'Tabloid' Chest furnished to Emin Pasha went through further vicissitudes. At the time the famous German was murdered, the Belgian explorer, Baron François Dhanis, was consolidating the Belgian possessions in Africa and establishing the supremacy of

Baron Dhanis

the Congo Free State. This hardy traveller had established several stations on the Middle Congo after the discoveries of Stanley. In 1890, he explored the Stanley Falls region as far as the River Kwango. His civilising activities were resented by Arab slave raiders. He attacked and captured several fortified Arab towns, and in 1893 routed the slavers utterly in the battle of Kasongo. Among the possessions left behind by the fleeing Arabs was the 'Tabloid' Chest supplied by Burroughs Wellcome & Co. to Emin Pasha. It was subsequently stolen from Baron Dhanis in turn; but, eventually, it was recovered near Kenia, in the Aruwhimi dwarf country and returned to Burroughs Wellcome & Co. *(see illustration No. 9, page 18).*

By courtesy of the Kenia Government

One of the 'Tabloid' Medicine Chests carried by Sir H. M. Stanley during the Emin Pasha Relief Expedition. Discovered in the Government Medical Store at Nairobi in 1932.

Another famous medicine chest, used during Stanley's travels, has an interesting history. This was his "Rear-Guard" 'Tabloid' Medicine Chest, which for nearly four years was left in the swampy forest regions of the Stanley's "Rear-Guard" Aruwhimi. More than once, it was actually under Chest water in the river. Eventually, it was found and brought back to England. Its remaining contents were tested by the official analyst of the *Lancet* (London, Eng.), one of the leading British medical papers, who reported that the 'Tabloid' Medicaments were in a perfect state of preservation *(see illustration No. 2, page 18).*

REV. A. B. LLOYD—A PIONEER AFRICAN MISSIONARY

Rev. A. B. Lloyd at one of his camps. He was a pioneer missionary and penetrated the Land of Dwarfs and the cannibal country of Central Africa

MRS. BISHOP (MISS ISABELLA BIRD)—PIONEER TRAVELLER AND AUTHOR

Dispensing medicines to natives of Persia. She travelled over a considerable portion of the uncivilised world and was regarded by the natives as a "Hakim," because of the 'Tabloid' Medicines she produced from her "magic box"

MISSIONARIES

No account of explorers would be complete without paying tribute to the invaluable pioneering work done by missionaries. David Livingstone, the most celebrated of them all in the 19th century, was by no means the only one. The missionary of to-day goes out not merely to make converts of Christianity; he goes also as a healer. Many missionaries are qualified medical practitioners.

In the past, as well as to-day, they have made, and are continuing to make, valuable scientific investigations. A considerable proportion of our geographical, anthropological and botanical knowledge comes from the intrepid missionaries, Roman Catholic and Protestant, who have gone to the far ends of the world to further their ministry.

Amongst the people to whom they have been sent they have spread not only the Gospel but also the principles of modern hygiene. Converting the natives to modern hygiene is frequently more difficult a task than converting them to Christianity. But the work goes on, slowly though inevitably, and in many remote parts the inhabitants have had cause to bless the healers that the religious bodies have sent out.

'Tabloid' Medical Equipments have been the choice of famous missionaries and of the foremost missionary organisations throughout the world, because it is recognised that not only do they enable effective medical treatment to be given in the most remote places but they are a valuable asset in securing the attention and goodwill of the natives to religious teaching. Missions and schools in the far north, in the Tropics, in Asia, Africa, South America, are equipped with 'Tabloid' First-Aid and 'Tabloid' Medical Outfits.

The medicine chest goes hand in hand with the advance of civilisation. The conquest of disease and the battle against ignorance and superstition are fought along the same frontiers.

COLONEL
THEODORE
ROOSEVELT
(1858–1919)
President of
the UNITED
STATES
(1901–1908)

One of the
'TABLOID'
MEDICINE CHESTS
supplied to
COLONEL THEODORE
ROOSEVELT
for
Expeditionary use

SOME OTHER HEROES OF TRAVEL

IN 1909, Colonel Theodore Roosevelt, the elder, who, during his Presidency, had been looking forward to the day when he might take a rest from statesmanship and follow one of his first loves—travelling—left New York for Africa to realise his long-felt ambition. He did not profess to be aiming at achievement as an explorer; he was just out after big game. Nevertheless, his expedition brought back much varied scientific information as well as zoological and botanical specimens.

It was his first expedition to Africa, but he had learned enough from his reading and his conversations with other great travellers to organise and equip his force completely. What he learned in Africa in 1909 stood him in good **Roosevelt** stead in 1914, when he organised his expedition to Brazil. On that occasion he explored a new river which was named after him, the Rio Teodoro. Until he mapped it, it had been known as the " River of Doubt. "

Lieutenant-Colonel Mearns, who was his first medical officer, states this about the 'Tabloid' Medical Equipments that the great Roosevelt took with him :—

"I wish to inform you that the equipment was most satisfactory in every way. The 'Tabloid' and 'Soloid' products, in addition to being convenient and compact, are extremely accurate and reliable. In this expedition the 'Tabloid' medical equipment never failed us, and is the most practicable it has been my pleasure to see or use."

RELIC 'TABLOID' MEDICINE CASES—TRAVEL, ETC.

1—Harry de Windt's Medical Equipment, used on his travels in E. Siberia. 2—Chest taken by the late President Roosevelt on his shooting and hunting expedition in East Africa. 3—Chest carried by Lionel Declé on his three years' journey from the Cape to Uganda (6000 miles). 4—Mrs. Bishop (Miss Isabella Bird), in her book describing her extensive wanderings, highly commends this Medicine Case. 5—The Medical Equipment carried by Mrs. French Sheldon, F.R.G.S., on her adventurous expedition throughout the entire Congo Free State. 6—Duplicate of Medicine Chest taken by Sven Hedin on his unique journey beyond the Himalayas into the heart of Tibet. 7—Case carried by R. L. Jefferson, F.R.G.S., on his famous bicycle ride to Khiva. 8—Pocket-Case carried by J. E. Budgett Meakin. 9—Medicine Chest carried by Julius Price, of the *Illustrated London News*, for over 30,000 miles through various climes.

By the time Colonel Roosevelt set out on his trek over Africa, the conditions of exploration in the so-called Dark Continent had been considerably changed. Every year they became less severe. Indeed, Carveth Wells, the brilliant Cornish lecturer and traveller, has declared that African exploration to-day is not nearly so dangerous as journeying in the Malay States, or in South America, or on the streets of New York. Mr. Wells is perhaps inclined to go out of his way to upset popular conceptions; but he is qualified to speak, because he followed in the footsteps of the Duke of the Abruzzi to the topmost peaks of the Ruwenzori range.

Carveth Wells also has written that far too little credit has been given to that intrepid but unassuming explorer, the Duke of the Abruzzi, a cousin of the King of Italy. After a distinguished naval career, he set himself to conquering Mount St. Elias in Alaska. Nobody had ever done it before, but he reached the top in 1897. Two years later, he led an expedition to the North Pole. He himself was detained by frost-bite at a Base Camp. But his second-in-command managed to reach 86 degrees 34 minutes North. That, in 1899, was the farthest that any man had ever attained. In 1906 the Duke of the Abruzzi was the first man to climb the twin peaks of Ruwenzori, a height of 16,800 feet. He not only climbed them; he came back with a detailed map of the range. In 1909, he attacked the Central Karakoram range in Northern India. On this effort, too, he reached a point higher than man had ever gone before—24,600 feet up Mount Godwin-Austen. The Duke of the Abruzzi was equipped by Burroughs Wellcome & Co. with a 'Tabloid' Medicine Chest.

One of the greatest names in the history of travel is that of the famous Swede, Dr. Sven Hedin. It is of him that Lord Morley remarked : " Hedin is a man with pity in him, with a sense of justice in him, with good temper in him. He raised no ill will anywhere." And those qualities account for the success of his wanderings all over Asia, including hitherto forbidden places.

C

Sven Hedin started his travels in 1885, through Persia and Mesopotamia. Five years later he visited the countries of Central Asia, countries mostly inhospitable to inspection by any European.

Sven Hedin

It was Sven Hedin who traced the mighty mountain palisade of the Trans-Himalaya. He discovered the sources of the Brahmaputra and the Indus. Also, Lake Chunitso and a great range of mountains north of the Himalaya, which to-day are named after him. He was the first white man to explore the Roof of the World in Tibet. In this connexion he tells of an interesting episode.

Sven Hedin's 'Tabloid' Medicine Chest was his trusted companion. It served him not only in illness and hardship, but in this emergency even helped him out diplomatically. At Shigatse he was afforded the privilege of an interview with the Tibetan potentate, the Tashi-Lama. We are indebted to Dr. Hedin's publishers, Messrs. Macmillan & Co., for permission to quote his account of the incident :—

> "When we had conversed for two hours I made a move to leave him, but the Tashi-Lama pushed me back on the chair and said, 'No, stay a little longer.' Now was the time to present my offering. The elegant English medicine chest was taken out of its silk cloth, opened and exhibited, and excited his great admiration and lively interest ; everything must be explained to him. The hypodermic syringe in its tasteful case, with all its belongings, especially delighted him. Two monks of the medical faculty were sent for several days running to write down in Tibetan the contents of the various 'Tabloid' Boxes and the use of the medicines."

Incidentally, the American Mission that went to Abyssinia in 1903, the first American expedition to that empire, also had an interesting report to make. A member of the Commission has written that the 'Tabloid' Medicine Chest that accompanied them was "a highly-valued resource in time of trouble. It was carried on the back of a faithful domestic, rejoicing in a name which, being translated, means 'Slave of the Holy Trinity.'"

One of the foremost contributors to our knowledge of South America is Dr. Alexander Hamilton Rice. This distinguished geographer, Vice-President of the American Geographical Society, Gold Medallist Royal Geographical Society, has conducted no fewer than seven expeditions into Colombia, Brazil and Venezuela. He has mapped the prodigious area of some 500,000 square miles of tropical South America. Incidentally, it was Dr. Rice who organised the Geographical Society's School of Geographical Surveying. In writing about his fifth expedition through the swamps of the Amazon, Dr. Rice remarked : " Everything supplied by Burroughs Wellcome & Co. has proved most satisfactory and efficient under most trying and adverse conditions of climate and stubborn cases of disease."

Hamilton Rice

When you think of the Gobi desert, the first name that comes into your mind is that of Roy Chapman Andrews, M.A., Sc.D., the man who discovered the dinosaur eggs. Dr. Andrews has put it on record that from his boyhood he yearned to be an explorer. He was trained as a naturalist. The moment he left Beloit College, Wisconsin, he went as fast as he could to the American Museum of Natural History. There he asked to be sent out on any old expedition. He was promptly told that he had no experience. Young Andrews replied that he did not expect to become a leader in 24 hours ; he would carry bundles, he would wash dishes, he would do anything. Against such a combination of determination and humility the heads of the Museum were powerless. In 1908 Roy Chapman Andrews was sent on an expedition to Alaska. A year later he was appointed the official naturalist aboard the U.S.S. "Albatross," on her scientific voyage to the Dutch East Indies. In 1911 and 1912 he explored Korea. It was in 1916 that he started the expeditions which have made him famous—the expeditions to investigate early animal and human life in Central Asia. On the third of these, in 1921–24, he discovered his dinosaur eggs and other remains and evidences of ancient animal and human existence.

Roy Chapman Andrews

Dr. Andrews to-day is Chief of the Division of Asiatic Exploration and Vice-Director of the Division of the American Museum of

Natural History. On all his expeditions, Dr. Andrews has depended on 'Tabloid' Medicine Equipment to maintain and protect the health of his staff. Every time he sets out on a new expedition he refills his old 'Tabloid' Cases with 'Tabloid' Medicines and Bandages to replace those used on previous trips. It was after he returned from finding his dinosaur eggs that he wrote to Burroughs Wellcome & Co. :—

"The 'Tabloid' Medicine Chest met every emergency admirably . . . . and we found the medicines in the case experienced no deterioration whatever, even though they passed through an extraordinary variety of climates and altitudes."

To mention all the travellers who have been thus equipped with 'Tabloid' Medicine Cases would be to call the roll of the Explorers' Club and the Geographical Societies of many countries. The names of many appear on other pages of this book. In addition, there may be mentioned those of Thomas Stevens, who travelled around the world on a bicycle; Jefferson, who rode by bicycle to Khiva; and Fraser Lunn and Lowe, who cycled round the world; Julius Price, the special artist and correspondent of the *Illustrated London News* (London, Eng.), Captain Stairs, Mrs. Bishop (Miss Isabella Bird), W. S. Caine, M.P., Mrs. French Sheldon, Glave, Muxworthy, Lovett Cameron, Dr. Charles Burland, Dr. Rendall and very many others. They have all endorsed the extreme portability and absolute reliability of 'Tabloid' Medicaments.

The Medical Officers of the great British Companies occupied in commercial enterprise abroad have been able to submit 'Tabloid' Equipments and 'Tabloid' Medicaments to thorough and exhaustive trials. Such reports as the following are therefore of particular interest :—

"We have had two chests fitted with 'Tabloid' Medicines in daily use during the occupation of the country. I think it only just to tell you they have proved of inestimable service.

Being quite portable, compact and readily accessible whilst upon the march, they have saved patients and myself much time and worry. I know of no medicine chests so admirably adapted to the wants of the traveller.''

R. F. RAND, M.D., F.R.C.S.
Principal Medical Officer, British South Africa Company.

"All these 'Tabloid' drugs are so good it is impossible for me to speak more highly of one than another. They are all of the best quality; each drug is accurately described and reliable. To the traveller these preparations are simply invaluable, and I would strongly advise everyone coming out to the Tropics to get a full supply of 'Tabloid' Medicines.''

W. H. CROSSE, M.D., M.R.C.S.
Principal Medical Officer, British Royal Niger Company.

Famous War Correspondents have carried 'Tabloid' Cases with Kitchener to Khartoum, in the Philippines, in Cuba, in the Balkans, and on all the fronts of the Great War, including Mesopotamia. For example, G. W. Steevens, the *Daily Mail* War Correspondent, used his 'Tabloid' Medicine Case throughout the Turco-Grecian War, during two Sudan campaigns, in India and in the Boer War.

MOUNT EVEREST

The most spectacular feat of this century so far has been the conquest of Mount Everest in the Himalayas, the highest mountain in the world. It took aeroplanes finally to accomplish this feat, but the attempts to do it on foot were notable exploits of gallantry, endurance and, above all, organisation.

Mount Everest presents a peculiar problem, or rather set of problems. Before its ascent could even be attempted, long diplomatic negotiations were necessary. The consent of the Lamas of Tibet and the government of India had to be obtained. In the matter of organisation, as many preparations were necessary as for a Polar Expedition. Large corps of porters had to be engaged, Base Camps and Way Camps planned and established.

MOUNT EVEREST—THE GREATEST HEIGHT CLIMBED BY MAN

Four attempts have been made to climb to the summit of Mount Everest. The record height achieved was 28,200 feet (1924). In the foreground, members of the Expedition are seen in their Base Camp on the Rongbuk Glacier (17,000 feet)

It was not until 1921 that, with great difficulty, permission was obtained from the rulers of Tibet. Then a preliminary Expedition, under Lieutenant-Colonel C. K. Howard Bury, D.S.O., was sent out to reconnoitre the ground and explore the valleys approaching Mount Everest. The first actual attempt was made in 1922, under the command of Brigadier-General the Hon. C. G. Bruce, C.B., M.V.O. On May 19, 1922, three members of this force climbed up to a point 26,985 feet above sea level, the highest so far attained by human beings. One week later, Captain G. I. Finch and Captain J. G. Bruce, with the help of oxygen masks, reached 27,300 feet. A third attempt, on June 7, ended in a frightful catastrophe. An avalanche thundered down the mountain side, sweeping away seven out of a party of nine porters. The Expedition was then abandoned.

Early attempts

In 1924, another Mount Everest Expedition, also under the command of General Bruce, achieved the record climbing height of 28,200 feet, at which altitude two members of the party, Mallory and Irvine, were last seen within 800 feet of the summit. On the return of this expedition, Major R. W. G. Hingston, the medical officer made the following report :—

Record climbing height

"I am having returned to the Mount Everest Committee the 'Tabloid' Chest of medicines and appliances which your firm has supplied to successive Mount Everest Expeditions. The Chest has been most successful. It has served with three successive Expeditions, and, though subjected to much ill-usage through transport, is still fit to do duty with a fourth.

"I have some experiences of the requirements of medical equipment, both on Himalayan Expeditions and on active service, and I know nothing which combines efficiency and portability better than does your 'Tabloid' Medicine Chest."

Rulyhingston

(R W. G. HINGSTON)

HOUSTON—MOUNT EVEREST FLIGHT

Houston-Westland aeroplane flying over Lhotse on its approach to
Mount Everest at a height of 32,000 feet on April 3, 1933

Inset, photograph of one of the 'Tabloid' First-Aid Outfits supplied
for aeroplane equipment

Early in 1933, the Houston—Mount Everest Expedition was organised to conquer the mountain from the air. The Expedition was under the command of Air-Commodore P. F. M. Fellowes. At 8.25 on the morning of April 3, 1933, two planes took off from Lalbalu. The first was piloted by Lord Clydesdale, the second-in-command of the Expedition. With him, as observer, Conquest of Everest by air was Colonel L. V. S. Blackner. The second plane was piloted by Flight-Lieutenant D. F. McIntyre. With him went S. R. Bonnett, the Chief Cinematographer of the Expedition. All four of them were equipped with oxygen masks. The only mishap was the breaking of Bonnett's oxygen tube. It rendered him unconscious for a while, but there were no fatal consequences. At five minutes past ten, Lord Clydesdale's plane, closely followed by McIntyre, flew over the summit of Mount Everest, clearing the peak by 100 feet. On the following day, Commodore P. F. M. Fellowes, the leader of the Expedition, flew over the neighbouring peak of Kanchenjunga. Later in the month, the Expedition was ordered back and any further flights were forbidden. But Fellowes had become stricken with fever and Second flight over summit was bedridden. While he was in that condition, his subordinates committed an act of what has since been called "magnificent insubordination." Orders or no orders, they made another flight, even more successful than the first one, on April 20, and procured superb photographs, which have since made possible a complete mapping of the region.

It will be appreciated that owing to the difficulties which, it was known, would be encountered, the selection of equipment for the Expedition had been made with the utmost attention to detail. It is a significant tribute, therefore, to the lightness, compactness and efficiency of 'Tabloid' First-Aid that one No. 244 and two No. 261 'Tabloid' First-Aid Outfits were selected—the former for use at the Base and the others for aircraft equipment.

'Tabloid' Medicine Chests and Reserve Medical Stores of 'Tabloid' Medicaments, Bandages, Dressings, etc., supplied by Burroughs Wellcome & Co., to the Mount Everest Expedition, 1933

Colonel P. T. Etherton, Secretary of the Houston—Mount Everest Expedition, reported :—

"With reference to the medicine cases supplied by you to the above Expedition, I wish to express our entire appreciation, and how very useful we found them on the aerial voyage from England to India, and during the stay of the Expedition at its base at Purnea, whence the flight over the world's highest mountain was made.

"In view of our experience of this excellent outfit, we consider that every Expedition should be similarly equipped."

(P. T. ETHERTON)

In May, 1933, a fourth climbing Expedition, led by Mr. Hugh Ruttledge, composed of an entirely different personnel, made the attempt. Their gallant efforts were blocked by snow and they were recalled by London. This was the first force to set out with radio equipment.

Mr. Ruttledge's medical officer reported :—

"The equipment was packed in two 'Tabloid' Aluminium Medicine Chests, fitted with featherweight unbreakable containers, reserves being packed in three-ply wood boxes. The equipment and the containers were extremely satisfactory."

To which report the leader appended his personal notation as follows :—

"I should like to add my appreciation of the excellent work done for the Expedition by Messrs. Burroughs Wellcome & Co."

(HUGH RUTTLEDGE)

So that is how 'Tabloid' Outfits shared in the conquest of the mightiest mountain in the world. We shall now consider how it came to pass that they were, literally, first at the North Pole and first at the South Pole.

REAR-ADMIRAL RICHARD E. BYRD, U.S.N. (Retired), 1888

NORTH POLE	...	...	...	May 6, 1926
AMERICA TO FRANCE	...	...	January 29/30, 1927
SOUTH POLE	...	...	...	November 29, 1929

Huffard Gold Medal; Congressional Medal of Honour; Distinguished Service Medal; The Flying Cross, etc.; Patron's Medal, Royal Geographical Society

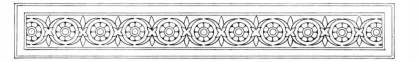

HEROES OF POLAR EXPLORATION

MODERN Arctic exploration began not so much with a search for the North Pole as for the North-West Passage. Like Columbus and those who followed him in more southerly waters, the navigators in the Arctic seas were hungry to find a short cut to the riches of Asia. It was to this end that Sir John Franklin and so many other gallant adventurers lost their lives, while hundreds more went through untold sufferings.

It seems eminently fitting that such a large proportion of success should have been achieved by Norsemen and their descendants. From Eric the Red down to Roald Amundsen the lust of battle with the rigours of northern seas, and the allure of the mysteries that lay behind barriers of ice and snow, have Early Norsemen been in the Norseman's blood. Amundsen has told in so many words what his feelings were after reading the books by and about Franklin. "What appealed to me most strongly," he wrote, "were the sufferings he and his men endured. A strange ambition burned within me to endure those same sufferings."

The early story is dim enough. Sailing from his home in Iceland in the 10th century, Eric the Red was beyond all doubt the first to establish a colony in Greenland. Eric's offspring, Leif Ericsson, set sail from that colony in Greenland and reached the coast of America 500 years before Cabot and Columbus.

The very difficulty of the North-West Passage made it more of a challenge than the North-East Passage, the mystery of which was solved in 1553 as the result of an expedition under the command of Sir Hugh Willoughby.

John Cabot, a well-to-do merchant of Bristol, England, sailing from Bristol in 1497, under Letters Patent from King Henry VIII, discovered Newfoundland and Labrador, likewise Cape Breton and Nova Scotia. He and his son Sebastian made other voyages, including one along both the east and west shores of Greenland. That was as far as Cabot got toward the North-West Passage.

It was almost a century later that Sir Martin Frobisher, sailing
northward around the Shetland Islands, almost
Frobisher   perished on the Coast of Greenland.   However, he
survived and reached Labrador.

The first man to follow Frobisher to the Arctic seas, John Davis,
was one of the most important navigators in the hunt for the
North-West Passage. He discovered the Strait that
Davis   bears his name, but did not get any further north
than 72 degrees 41 minutes.

When Henry Hudson first sailed up what is now New York
Harbour in 1609, he, too, was looking for the North-West Passage.
The following year, making use of the information acquired by
Davis, he sailed through Davis Strait.   But his most momentous
expedition was in 1610. On that journey he made first
Hudson   for Greenland, then discovered Hudson Strait.   When
he entered the great Bay now known as Hudson Bay, he thought he
had reached the Pacific Ocean.   He planned to pass the winter on the
shores of Hudson Bay.   But his men mutinied and cast him adrift
with eight others.   Incidentally, the ringleaders of the mutineers
perished, and it was only after terrific sufferings that the other few
survivors got back to England.

Hudson's idea that the bay he had found was the Pacific Ocean
was disproved by William Baffin, who discovered another Bay,
which now bears his name.

With the dawning of the 19th century, travellers, mostly of
British origin, began to set up records farther and farther north.
It was Sir William Edward Parry, sailing on the ''Hecla'' in 1818,
who left the first record of an expedition in which
Parry   some attempt had been made at medical equipment.
and Ross   Parry also was the first to make an organised attempt to
reach the North Pole in dog sleds from Spitzbergen.   He led no less
than four expeditions, the third of which was wrecked.   On his fourth
he got as far as 82 degrees 45 minutes north.   In 1827 John Ross and
his nephew, James Ross, made a great Arctic journey, in the course
of which the latter reached the northern point of King William
Land, which he named Cape Felix.   James Ross, on a second journey,
planted the British flag at the North Magnetic Pole.

FRANKLIN AND GREELY

In all the history of exploration, the two most poignant dramas are those of the Englishman, Sir John Franklin, and the American, General Adolphus Washington Greely. The principal difference between them is that General Greely lived to tell the tale—indeed, he is alive to-day—while Franklin perished with all his men.

SIR JOHN FRANKLIN, F.R.S., 1786–1847

John Franklin entered the British navy as a first-class volunteer at the age of fourteen years, and, after experience in naval battles under Nelson and a voyage of exploration in southern seas, set sail in 1818 on an expedition to the North Pole, led by Commander David Buchan. They had one ship of 570 tons and another of 250 and provisions for two years. They got no further than 80 degrees 34 minutes north.

But Franklin's next voyage was more successful. This time he shared the command with Dr. Richardson, a scientist. They proceeded to Hudson Bay on one of the ships of the Hudson Bay Company and were nearly wrecked. However, they reached York Factory and stayed there three months, making observations. They then took one of the Company's transports, about 40 feet long, and made their way laboriously up the Steel River. After two months they landed at Cumberland House, 700 miles away, on the Saskatchewan River. Over a period of almost two years, they travelled 5550 miles before returning to York Factory. In the course of that time they had built Fort Enterprise and made many discoveries of importance. They were on the verge of starvation when they staggered, exhausted, back to York Factory. In his absence, Franklin had been promoted to the rank of Commander in the Royal Navy, and on his return, for his contributions to science, was made a Post Captain and a Fellow of the Royal Society.

Franklin's next expedition struck a course overland. His chief accomplishment was to trace the coast of North America as far as 149 degrees 37 minutes west. For this, he received a knighthood from the British Crown and a gold medal from the Geographical Society of Paris.

Franklin's great adventure began in 1845. A Rear-Admiral by this time, he was appointed to the command of an expedition the main purpose of which was, once more, to find the North-West Passage. The last that was seen of him alive was on July 26, 1845, when a whaling ship sighted his squadron in Baffin Bay, about 74 degrees 48 minutes north and 66 degrees 13 minutes west. All through 1846 and 1847 there were no tidings of the Franklin Expedition. The British Government, the country, indeed most of the civilised world, became alarmed. Lady Franklin was frantic. The first rescue expedition was sent out at her expense in 1848. This was under the command of Sir James Ross. Second in command was Robert (later Sir Robert) McClure, who was destined to become the first explorer to pass through the North-West Passage. Only three graves were found, but Lady Franklin was indefatigable. Rewards were offered and one expedition after another, both English and American, went out to look for the missing Franklin. A total of £982,000 of English money was spent in this search, while in America some $250,000 were laid out. Incidentally, the expeditions that went to rescue Franklin brought back a vast store of geographical and other scientific information.

The most important American Expedition was that of Dr. Elisha Kent Kane, a naval officer and scholar of Philadelphia. He was financed by Henry Grinnell, a wealthy Philadelphian, whose name will be found on maps of the Arctic regions. Dr. Kane led two

expeditions, the second of which started in May, 1853.   For a while
it was thought that he and his men had perished.   For two years
no news came of them.   In the very first year they
were frozen off the north-west coast of Greenland.   Rescue
In the second year their fresh food gave out.   The   efforts
party was attacked by scurvy.   Kane and his men finally reached
safety after a terrific trip on foot for 83 miles down the Greenland
coast, at the end of which they were met by a rescue party.

Previously to the Grinnell-Kane Expedition, however, others had
set out from England, one of them under the command of the veteran,
Sir John Ross, uncle of Sir James Ross.   In 1851, Captain Ommanney
found Franklin's winter quarters on Beechey Island, where, as it
later turned out, he had abandoned his ships.

The suspense and drama of the situation became more acute.
In 1854, Dr. Rae, trekking with dog sleds from Repulse Bay, brought
back various articles identified as having belonged to Franklin's
party, and a tale of white men dragging a boat laboriously along the
west shore of King William's Island.   In 1855 another British Government Expedition went down the MacKenzie River in canoes.   Their
report led to the Government giving up all efforts to find Franklin.

Lady Franklin was not content.   In July, 1857, she financed
Captain (afterwards Sir Leopold) McClintock in the "Fox."
So began the famous voyage of the "Fox," which lasted two years.
It was not until the spring of 1859 that Captain
McClintock found skeletons and other remains on   Franklin's
King William's Island.   A little later he came upon   remains
a cairn at Point Victory, in which were records telling   found
the entire history of the Expedition up to April,
1848.   These records disclosed the fact that Franklin had died of
scurvy in June, 1847.   At that time no fewer than nine other officers
and men had perished.   The officers left in command—Captains
Crozier and Fitzjames—tried to make their way back to inhabited
parts, but died, presumably of scurvy and starvation.   An Eskimo
woman told Captain McClintock a harrowing tale of men, white as
ghosts, who fell down and died as they walked.   McClintock was able
to establish that Franklin had actually found the North-West Passage,

though it was left to Sir Robert McClure to sail all the way through it and prove that it was commercially impracticable. McClintock was knighted when he returned to England and promoted to Flag rank.

Adolphus Washington Greely, an army officer, was sent out in 1881, under the auspices of the United States Government, the Smithsonian Institution and several other scientific bodies, to make scientific observations at the head of Smith Sound. It was the result of an international agreement to establish scientific observation stations in the Arctic. He had no difficulty in reaching his destination on Grinnell Land. Before

Greely

GENERAL ADOLPHUS WASHINGTON GREELY
(Born 1844)

Greely left, full arrangements had been made for a relief vessel to be sent with supplies every summer until they returned. But in the summer of 1882, no relief vessel appeared. A vessel had been sent, but returned with its mission unfulfilled. In 1883, again no relief vessel arrived. It had been caught in the ice and sunk. Greely meanwhile had abandoned his post at Fort Conger in Grinnell Land and painfully made his way southward in boats. At a point near Cape Sabine, the party found a few supplies and a message left by the Relief Expedition promising success the following year.

When the second Relief Expedition failed, the Government at Washington gave up all hope, believing it was impossible for any members of the party to have survived. But, in fact, they were still alive, though frequently on the verge of starvation. The few remaining rations had to be conserved by the strictest rules. Rigid army discipline was enforced. Man after man died of hunger. The last issue of rum was made on May 24. About that time all were reduced to eating the sealskin thongs used to lash the sleds.

Meanwhile, public opinion in the United States had been aroused to high pitch by the failure to rescue Greely. Mrs. Greely had appealed to Douglas Gunn, editor of a newspaper in San Diego. Gunn, in turn, appealed to all editors in the country to join in the campaign. The rescue of Greely became **Public** a topic of first importance. The entire Press of the **opinion** country was aroused at the failure of the Government **aroused** to send relief. Every reader was begged to write to his Congressman and demand action. Chandler, Secretary of the Navy, was favourable to the enterprise. Finally, Congress appropriated money for the expedition and offered a prize of $25,000 for anyone who discovered Greely's party. On February 18, 1884, an expedition of three ships was sent out under the command of Commander Winfield Scott Schley, later to be the destroyer of a Spanish fleet in the Spanish-American War. On May 1 the rescuers had reached St. John, New Brunswick. By June 22, most of the marooned party had given up all hope. It was only the indomitable will of Greely that kept them alive. On that day, the few survivors had had nothing to eat or drink for 42 hours except a little sealskin soaked in water. They were haggard, weak and filthy.

On that evening Greely heard the sound of a steamer-whistle blowing three times. Two surviving members of his party crawled laboriously up a hill to the place where a flag of distress had been erected. But the flag had blown down. **Schley** They rolled down the hill to report to Greely, saying **rescues** that they had seen no signs of a steamer. Again they **Greely** were in despair, when suddenly they heard the sound of footsteps. Then voices called: "Greely! Are you there?" If Commander Schley had been 48 hours later, not a soul would have been alive. As it was, he brought seven men back to civilisation. Some of them were so weak they could hardly talk, let alone walk. Lieutenant Greely first knew he had been promoted when Commander Schley addressed him as "Major." He is now a General

DR. NANSEN—PIONEER ARCTIC EXPLORER

Dr. Nansen, one of the pioneers of Arctic exploration, starting from
"The Fram" on the sledge journey which gave him the contemporary
record of "Farthest North," 1893–96

DUC D'ABRUZZI—PIONEER ITALIAN POLAR EXPEDITION

An incident in the historic journey during which 86° 33′ 49″, the record
Northern latitude at that date (1899), was reached

and a prominent member of the Smithsonian Institution, and, in addition to the honours, possesses the Gold Medal of the Royal Geographical Society awarded to him in 1886.

One important fact was learned, or perhaps one should say re-learned, from the experience of the Greely party. They had started out with the last word in scientific equipment and copious supplies, but had not been supplied with adequate medical equipment. Of course, this fact alone was not responsible for the misfortunes and sufferings. Nevertheless, adequate medical supplies would have been most useful in alleviating at least some of the awful distress that preceded the rescue. Greely passed through extraordinary trials. His heroism and fortitude enabled him to survive them.

It may be remembered that shortly prior to the sailing of Greely's Expedition, the firm of Burroughs Wellcome & Co. had already issued 'Tabloid' Medical Equipments specially prepared to meet the needs of explorers. The reputation of these outfits soon spread all over the world. Subsequent to the disasters which befell the Greely Expedition, and which were prevented from reaching complete tragedy only by the courage and capacity of its leader, practically every explorer of note was equipped with a 'Tabloid' Outfit.

The next famous name in Arctic history is that of Fridtjof Nansen. Apart from his achievements as an explorer and scientist, Dr. Nansen also, in later years, earned **Nansen** a sound reputation as a statesman, notably in the cause of peace. In 1922 he received the Nobel Peace Prize.

As for his achievements in the Arctic, Amundsen and others have testified that, although Nansen himself never reached the Pole, he laid the groundwork for the success of Peary in the north and Amundsen in the south. He got as far as 86 degrees 14 minutes north. His ship, the "Fram," was built under his personal supervision, and from it many others learned how to construct vessels that would withstand the tremendous pressure of the ice. Incidentally, Nansen, in all his attempts at the Pole, carried with him a 'Tabloid' Medicine Chest.

One other drama of Polar exploration was that of Dr. Salomon August Andrée. This Swedish scientist got his first taste of exploration as a member of the Swedish Meteorological Expedition in 1882.

In the following years he made a careful study of the efforts of Dr. Nansen and others to get to the Pole. Dr. Andrée came to the conclusion that these long treks on foot were too expensive,

Andrée

took too long, and probably could not succeed. So he conceived the idea of making the venture by balloon. He developed the idea that a balloon might be stabilised by long ropes trailing in the water and navigated by the manipulation of sails. The idea of this form of stabiliser was, later on, adopted and elaborated by Walter Wellman.

Andrée built his balloon and stocked it completely. His only medical equipment was a 'Tabloid' Outfit. On July 11, 1897, he started from Danes Island. A few days after, some sailors on a whaling vessel were surprised to observe a pigeon and shot the bird. It turned out to be a carrier-pigeon released by Andrée, containing a message, which was subsequently relayed to Stockholm. That was the last message from Dr. Andrée. Numerous searching parties were sent out, but no trace of him could be found. In November, 1897, a band of sailors, shipwrecked at Spitzbergen, thought they heard cries of distress ; but the searching parties did not come upon any sign of Dr. Andrée. In 1898 and 1899, expeditions made a thorough search of the coasts of Northern Asia and the islands of New Siberia, but without avail. Later on, Dr. Nathorst sought in vain up and down the shores of East Greenland. Dr. Andrée had taken some buoys with him, in the hope of being able to convey messages thereby. Several of these were found, but only two of them contained messages, and they were dated on the day of the ascent.

This tragic disappearance, which remained a mystery for 33 years, was solved by accident. On August 6, 1930, some members of a Norwegian Scientific Expedition were hunting walrus on White Island, east of North-East Island in the Spitzbergen group. Peering over a ledge, they saw a boat hook sticking up in the snow. They investigated further and came across a book in a remarkably well-preserved condition. It was the diary of Dr. Andrée. Later on, they found a canvas boat marked ''Andrée's Polar Expedition, 1897.'' Naturally, this caused great excitement. A further search was made which resulted in the finding of the bodies of Dr. Andrée and his two companions, frozen stiff, and consequently in a perfect state of preservation.

Andrée's diary disclosed the details of the tragedy. The balloon had floated north of 83 degrees. On July 13, two days after they had started, they were forced to land and abandon their balloon. They marched over the ice, but perished, one by one, of cold and exposure. Apparently their supplies of fuel were exhausted. The bodies were taken back to Stockholm and given a public funeral.

Walter Wellman was really ahead of his time. That is, he was the first man who tried to get to the Pole by dirigible and failed because aerial navigation was then in too imperfect a stage of development. Wellman was originally a newspaper man by profession. He became interested in discovery in 1892, when, by exceedingly clever research, he found evidence which appeared to indicate that the spot on which Columbus had first landed was Watling Island.

This whetted his appetite for exploration, and in 1894 he led an Arctic Expedition which reached a point north-east of Spitzbergen at latitude 81 degrees. In 1908 he tried it again, going by way of Franz Joseph Land, getting as far as latitude 82 degrees north. In this attempt he discovered many new islands. In 1906, he persuaded Frank Noyes, publisher of the *Washington Star*, to finance him to the extent of $75,000 for an airship to carry him to the Pole. He had the dirigible, America I, built for him in Paris. He started from Danes Island, off Spitzbergen, but came to grief, though the balloon was not wrecked. Before he could make another attempt, the news came of Peary's success.

Nevertheless, Wellman rebuilt his airship, this time with the idea of attempting the first transatlantic crossing by air. He did not get across the Atlantic, but he did establish a world's record of 1010 miles. He was picked up at sea and brought back safely. He died at the age of 75 in February, 1934. He reports:—

"'Tabloid' Medical Equipment was the only one carried in the airship 'America' during one thousand miles' flight over the Atlantic Ocean. We had several occasions to use its contents for minor troubles, and found it complete and wholly satisfactory, which was but repeating the experience I have had with your equipments on my expeditions to the Arctic regions.''

Walter Wellman

(WALTER WELLMAN)

ADMIRAL R. E. PEARY
(1856–1920)

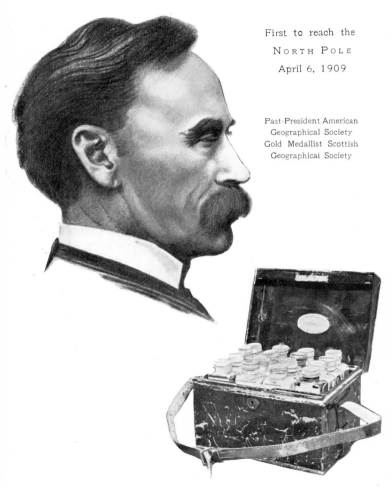

First to reach the
NORTH POLE
April 6, 1909

Past-President American
Geographical Society
Gold Medallist Scottish
Geographical Society

ONE OF ADMIRAL PEARY'S NORTH POLAR
'TABLOID' MEDICINE CHESTS

PEARY

The exploits of Admiral Robert E. Peary are probably too well known to need repeating here at length. He thoroughly earned the name of "Persevering Peary." His first important contribution to Polar science was to prove that Greenland was an island. Then he established the fact that the Polar ice cap extends no farther than 82 degrees north. He also settled rumours of rich iron mines in the Arctic. He discovered that the so-called mine was actually a meteorite, the largest in existence. Six times Robert E. Peary attempted what is curiously described as a "dash" to the Pole. Six times he was beaten back, but always after a greater measure of success, always with more knowledge how to succeed the next time. Finally, on September 6, 1909, the world learned that Peary had actually reached the Pole on April 6 of that year. Congress conferred on Robert E. Peary, quite justly, the rank of Admiral.

Tube of 'Tabloid' products carried by Admiral Peary to the NORTH POLE

When he returned, Admiral Peary presented to Burroughs Wellcome & Co. specimens of 'Tabloid' products that he had carried with him to the Pole. He had previously written from his base at Etah, Greenland, saying :—

"Burroughs Wellcome & Co.'s 'Tabloid' Medicine Cases and supplies have proven invaluable."

In a report sent in after a previous Expedition, he had conveyed his "appreciation of the wonderful compactness and utility of your products." So it was that 'Tabloid' products won the distinction of being first at the North Pole.

PEARY MONUMENT, ARLINGTON NATIONAL CEMETERY, WASHINGTON, D.C. Commemoration of the Twenty-Fifth Anniversary of the Discovery of the North Pole. At the close of the ceremonies taps was sounded over the grave of Admiral Robert E. Peary in the Arlington National

Another distinguished name in the records of the Arctic is that of Vilhjalmur Stefansson. He was born in Canada, but educated at the Universities of North Dakota and Iowa, studied anthropology at Harvard and was an instructor there for two years. His first work in the field was a series of archæological researches he made in Iceland. He also conducted an ethnological

Stefansson

survey of the central Arctic coast of the shores of North America. In 1913, when the Canadian Government was organising the Canadian Arctic Expedition, Mr. Stefansson was put in charge. His task was to explore the regions west of the Parry Archipelago. With a force of only two men and six dogs he made a journey of 96 days over the moving ice pack, making valuable additions to the geography of those regions. He also discovered new land north of Prince Patrick Island.

Personally, Stefansson makes a point of believing only what he can prove and of disproving popular misconceptions. So a tribute from him is of particular value. In 1916, Mr. Stefansson wrote from his base at Banks Island :—

"In that section of which I have been in personal charge, we have fortunately had no serious illness so far, but the practical utility of the 'Tabloid' First-Aid Equipment which we carried was proved on the occasion of an accident which nearly proved fatal to Captain Bernard. This equipment met the emergency well.

"The 'Tabloid' medicaments were found more satisfactory, both in portability and keeping qualities, than others of which we have had experience."

Vilhjalmur Stefansson

(VILHJALMUR STEFANSSON)

Photograph by Mr. H. G. Ponting, F.R.G.S., F.R.P.S., F.Z.S.

CAPTAIN ROBERT FALCON SCOTT, R.N., C.V.O., D.Sc., F.R.G.S.
(1868–1912)

South Pole, January 17, 1912

Gold Medallist, Royal Geographical Society; Royal Scottish Geographical Society; and
of the American, Swedish, Danish, Philadelphia and Antwerp Geographical Societies

ANTARCTIC ADVENTURES

The history of the Antarctic is astonishingly briefer than that of the North Pole. There is but little to tell of all the centuries before Scott, Shackleton, Mawson, Amundsen and Byrd came upon the scene. The tale begins with Captain Cook, who was the first man to cross the Antarctic Circle in 1773. Some 50 years later, the Russian Admiral, Bellingshausen, was the first to dip below the Antarctic Circle and discover land. This naval officer raised the Russian flag on Peter Island and Alexander Land. He got no farther than 70 degrees south. In 1841, Sir James Ross, whose exploits in the north we have already considered, discovered the great Ice Barrier as well as Mounts Erebus and Terror. It was not until 1895 that any human being set foot on the virgin Antarctic Continent. That was the Norwegian, Carsten Borchgrevink. In 1898, Sir George Newnes, founder and publisher of the *Strand Magazine*, organised the "Southern Cross Expedition," and put Borchgrevink in command. This veteran of the ice effected a landing at Cape Adare on South Victoria Land, February 7, 1899. He spent almost a year there, exploring and making scientific observations.

First landing on Antarctic Continent

If the South Pole attracted less attention from explorers, it also took eminently less toll in human lives and suffering. In fact, the first leader to give his life was Captain Robert Falcon Scott. But this did not happen until after he had made important contributions to the knowledge of the region and had actually reached the Pole. In 1901, he was put in command of the Royal Geographical Society's Antarctic Expedition, sometimes known as the "Discovery" Expedition, because of the name of their doomed ship that was crushed by the ice. In three years, Scott got farther than any other explorer up to that time. He passed the easternmost point attained by Sir James Ross in 1841. Then he crossed the great Ice Barrier which Ross had discovered, and

Scott

found that in 60 years it had crept 30 miles south. On and on, beyond the Barrier, he went. Scott's great journey took him 380 miles towards the Pole, to the record latitude of 82 degrees 17 minutes south. Then he discovered King Edward VII Land, and, with his dog teams, he trekked over glacier-covered Victoria Land. Scott, before he started, had been well-grounded in the principles of organisation for Polar adventure. Following the examples of Nansen and Peary, he took with him a 'Tabloid' Medical Equipment. A report was received from the President of the Royal Geographical Society, which read :—

CAPT. R. F. SCOTT, R.N. (1868-1912)

"The Medical Equipment of the Exploring Ship of the National Antarctic Expedition was entirely supplied by Messrs. Burroughs Wellcome & Co., and proved in every way most satisfactory.

"The few other drugs and preparations which were taken with the Expedition were only supplied for purposes of experiment, and can in no way be regarded as part of the medical equipment."

To which Dr. Edward A. Wilson, Scott's medical officer, who was also in charge of some of the dog sled trips made from the " Discovery, " added the following :—

"Though there was but little serious illness on the 'Discovery' during the recent Antarctic Expedition, the 'Tabloid' preparations and the cases were put to a fairly rigorous test, not only in the ship, but on the various sledge journeys that were undertaken, during which they experienced temperatures as low as 68° below zero, and much rough handling, without any loss in efficiency and usefulness. Certain of the 'Tabloid' Ophthalmics were freely used for snow blindness, and were found to be most convenient.''

Edward A. Wilson.

(EDWARD A. WILSON)

At this point Ernest Henry Shackleton enters the Antarctic picture in a big way. He had sailed under Scott, but until that time had had no Polar experience. Previously, he had been an officer in the British Mercantile Marine. Shackleton was taken ill and was obliged to return home.

SIR ERNEST SHACKLETON
FIRST TO REACH THE SOUTH MAGNETIC POLE
The party from the Expedition at the South Magnetic Pole
During this Expedition the ''Farthest South'' then reached by man
was attained, 88° 23′ (January 9, 1909)

Shackleton subsequently procured backing for an expedition of his own, and, in 1907, he set sail from New Zealand in the '' Nimrod.'' For all that his experience was so limited, Shackleton accomplished

CAPTAIN
ROALD AMUNDSEN
(1872–1928)

North-West Passage and North
Magnetic Pole, 1903–6
South Pole, December 14, 1911
North Pole, May 12, 1926

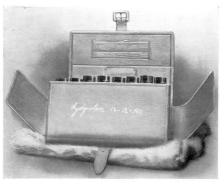

'TABLOID'
MEDICINE CASE
carried by
CAPTAIN AMUNDSEN
to the South Pole, inscribed
and dated by him

'Tabloid' products were the
only medicines actually carried
by Captain Amundsen to the
South Pole

an extraordinary feat.   He beat Scott's record, reached a point
88 degrees 23 minutes south latitude and planted the Union Jack
on the tip-top of Mount Gauss, 97 miles from the South Pole.
Another record made during this Expedition was that the South
Magnetic Pole was reached by a party of three,
amongst whom was Douglas (later Sir Douglas)   South
Mawson, who subsequently led the Australian   Magnetic
Antarctic Expedition, 1911, which added to the map   Pole
King George V and Queen Mary Land and accomplished very
important oceanographic work.   Sir Douglas expressed his "complete satisfaction with the 'Tabloid' Medical Equipment which
constituted the entire supply of drugs and surgical dressings."
Upon his return to England, Shackleton received the honour of
knighthood.

Shackleton's sole medical equipment on the "Nimrod," as
on his subsequent Expeditions, was a 'Tabloid' Outfit, on which
he reported :—

"The British Antarctic Expedition, 1907-9, was equipped
with a very complete Medical Equipment contracted for solely
by Messrs. Burroughs Wellcome & Co., and consisting of
'Soloid' and 'Tabloid' preparations, which are the only
forms that can be conveniently carried and preserved under
such conditions.

"All the 'Tabloid' products that remain are now in as good
condition as when first handed over to my care two years ago."

E. H. Shackleton

(ERNEST HENRY SHACKLETON, KT., C.V.O.)

Before we return to Captain Scott, we should consider Roald
Amundsen, because the stories of the two are closely interwoven.
Amundsen was born at Oslo, and the zest for Polar
exploration was in his blood.   Almost the first books   Amundsen
he read were the accounts of the voyages of Franklin and other
travellers.   As a youth, he deliberately set out to gain experience of
travel in snow and ice.   A few miles from Oslo, there is a plateau

E

CAPTAIN ROALD AMUNDSEN—FIRST TO REACH THE
SOUTH POLE

Amundsen and his four companions at the South Pole, which they
reached on December 14, 1911

CAPTAIN R. F. SCOTT—FIRST ENGLISHMAN TO REACH THE
SOUTH POLE

Captain Scott and his companions at the Base Camp. His ship, the
" Terra Nova," and Mount Erebus are shown in the background. Captain
Scott, with four companions, reached the South Pole, January 17, 1912

6000 feet high, and there Amundsen got his first practice. He also studied navigation and shipped before the mast on a sailing vessel to gain practical experience.

In 1897, he took part in the Belgian-Antarctic Expedition. The purpose was to make observations at the South Magnetic Pole.

In June, 1903, Amundsen took part in an expedition to make observations at the North Magnetic Pole. After two years on this task he brought back a wealth of scientific data.

In 1909, he bought the " Fram," Nansen's famous ship. His aim was the North Pole. But, before he started, the world was electrified by the news that Peary had got there first. This did not disconcert Amundsen; he continued equipping the "Fram" and procured a large number of the best dogs he could buy. He set sail in an atmosphere of mystery. When the "Fram" reached Madeira, he announced his intentions to his companions. They were going to the South Pole! At the same time, he took particular care to send a cable to Captain Scott, who was then in Australia preparing for a similar venture, notifying Scott of his plans.

In all these years, Amundsen had made the most intensive study and had had sound practical experience of travelling in the Frigid Zone. He was convinced that dog sleds provided the only really practical means of attaining the goal. Captain Scott, however, had conceived another theory. He had fitted himself out with motor sleds and Shetland ponies.

When Amundsen reached the Bay of Whales, he set up his camp there. A detachment from Captain Scott's party visited him. When Amundsen learned that Scott contemplated reaching the South Pole with motor sleds and Shetland ponies, he shook his head and gallantly offered Scott half of his dogs. Scott's record sledge journey The offer was refused. So the rivals set out, each in his own fashion, in the race to the South Pole. The Englishman achieved an extraordinary feat. He made the longest continuous sledge journey in history, 1842 miles. He reached the South Pole, January 17, 1912, only to find that Amundsen had beaten him to it by over four weeks.

Incidentally, both Amundsen and Scott carried 'Tabloid' Outfits. So, whichever one of them had won, the 'Tabloid' Equipment would have been the first at the South Pole as at the North Pole. Amundsen reported :—

"I have much pleasure in testifying to the efficiency of the 'Tabloid' Brand Medical Equipment with which you supplied me in 1910. All the medicines were most beautifully packed, and everything kept well.

"The brown leather Case which I returned to you was the only one I actually carried with me to the South Pole, and I have much pleasure in sending it back to you as a souvenir of my journey.

"I shall always consider one of your equipments as indispensable for either Arctic or Antarctic travels."

(ROALD AMUNDSEN, CAPT.)

In his book, "The South Pole," Captain Amundsen notes that the 'Tabloid' Equipment was unaffected by cold and damp. "It was splendid in every way," he reported.

Captain Scott reached the South Pole on January 17, 1912, whereas Amundsen was there on December 14, 1911. On the return, Scott and his four heroic companions succumbed. Evans died from concussion. Oates, the "very gallant English Gentleman," sacrificed himself, hoping thereby to save his friends. Scott, Bowers and Wilson perished through exhaustion and cold. Scott's last diary, telling the story of the fight against a nine days' blizzard with only two days' supply of food and fuel, was found in his tent, eight months later, together with a 'Tabloid' Medicine Case.

CAPT. L. E. G. OATES

Here is the final entry in the diary, dated March 29, 1912 :—

"We had fuel to make two cups of tea apiece and bare food for two days on the 20th. Every day we have been ready to start for our depot eleven miles away, but outside the door of the tent it remains a scene of whirling drift. I do not think we can hope for any better things now. We shall stick it out to the end, but we are getting weaker, of course, and the end cannot be far.

" It seems a pity but I do not think I can write more."

(ROBERT F. SCOTT, CAPT., C.V.O.)

Scott's achievements were no less great because he did not live to hear the plaudits of his fellow-men of all nations. The splendour

'TABLOID' MEDICINE CASE
Carried by SCOTT to the South Pole and found in the tent in which he died

of his courage, pain endured without murmur, death faced without flinching, adds glory to the record of his work for exploration and science.

It is interesting to recall that Mr. H. G. Ponting, the Photographic Officer to this Expedition, developed all his negatives in the Antarctic with 'Tabloid' 'Rytol' Developer.

Sir Ernest Shackleton's ambition had been to excel his own record and reach the South Pole, but, when the news of Amundsen and Scott was received, he organised the Imperial Trans-Antarctic Expedition, and, in 1914, set sail in a vessel that he had named the "Endurance." This, also, was fitted out with 'Tabloid' Medical Equipments. Its value, as well as the purpose of the Expedition, is summarised in the following letter written by Sir Ernest :—

"I am happy to send you information regarding the medical equipment of the Imperial Trans-Antarctic Expedition, 1914, of which you were the sole suppliers. You supplied us with a special portable outfit for the projected journey across the plateau from the Weddell to the Ross Sea, in addition to the medical and surgical equipments for the S.S. "Endurance" and S.S. "Aurora." From my own experience, confirmed by the reports of the medical officers of the Expedition, I have pleasure in stating that these equipments proved in every way satisfactory and were eminently suited to the purpose for which they were intended.

"The Expedition also employed 'Tabloid' Photographic Chemicals, the value and reliability of which were amply demonstrated."

E.H.Shackleton

(ERNEST HENRY SHACKLETON, KT., C.V.O)

The "Endurance" was caught in the ice, and, after drifting for eight months, sank, owing to ice pressure, on November 21, 1915. The whole party encamped on an ice floe, but were obliged to take to the boats on the disintegration of the ice pack in the following April. They reached Elephant Island safely, but exhausted. Shackleton rose to the occasion magnificently and led a forlorn hope in the endeavour to reach South Georgia, 840 miles away. With five companions he accomplished the wonderful feat in spite of raging seas. He reached the island in 14 days and then completed his heroic task by crossing unknown mountains and glaciers to find succour for the three men left with the boat and the party left behind on Elephant Island.

Shackleton's next voyage was his last. In 1922, he set out in the "Quest," at the head of the Shackleton-Rowett Expedition. His purpose was to cover some 30,000 miles in the South Atlantic and Antarctic. Evidently he had contracted influenza Shackleton-Rowett Expedition before he left. When he reached Grytviken, a whaling point on South Georgia Island, he was seriously ill. Curiously enough, Grytviken had been the jumping-off point for the Imperial Trans-Antarctic Expedition of 1914. Sir Ernest Henry Shackleton died of angina pectoris, an aftermath of his attack of influenza, in September, 1922, with his last task unaccomplished.

Captain L. Hussey, who was medical officer to Sir Ernest Shackleton's South Polar Expedition, was with him on the "Quest" when he died, and conveyed his body to its last resting-place in South Georgia. Captain Hussey had previously been medical officer to one of Sir Henry Wellcome's Archæological Expeditions in the Sudan.

The Shackleton-Rowett Expedition was also equipped with a 'Tabloid' First-Aid Equipment; and Mr. Frank Wild, one of the leaders of the party, wrote as follows :—

> "There is little that can be said which will add to the high reputation your products already have, and I can only repeat what has been my experience on every one of the five expeditions in which I have taken part, viz., that your equipments and products gave every satisfaction and functioned equally well in tropic heat and antarctic cold. For compactness, reliability and general usefulness, they stand in a class by themselves."

Frank Wild

(FRANK WILD)

POLAR FLIGHTS

In 1914, Amundsen bought a Farman biplane, with the intention of flying to the North Pole. But, in 1914, the Great War broke out, and he gave his plane to the Norwegian Government. His next feat, starting in 1918, was to drift clear across the Arctic Ocean through the North-East Passage. This he accomplished by July, 1920, landing at Nome, Alaska.

Lincoln Ellsworth, who now has quite an independent reputation of his own as an explorer, financed Amundsen in a seaplane flight from Spitzbergen over the Pole. This one failed. They were forced to turn back after going 600 miles. Then they learned that the Italian Government was willing to sell the Dirigible N 1, which had been designed and   The "Norge" constructed under the supervision of General Di Nobile. The sale was made and the ship was re-christened the "Norge." It was suggested that as Di Nobile had designed the airship he should be engaged as navigator. To this both Captain Amundsen

REAR-ADMIRAL BYRD
AND
CAPTAIN AMUNDSEN
AT
SPITZBERGEN

Amundsen is carrying the 'Tabloid' Medicine Case taken by Byrd on his flight over the North Pole

and Lincoln Ellsworth consented. They started from Spitzbergen in May, 1926, in the "Norge," and accomplished a record flight over the North Pole to Teller in Alaska, after a journey of only 72 hours.

AMUNDSEN–ELLSWORTH—THE FIRST AIRSHIP VOYAGE TO THE NORTH POLE

The "Norge," with Captain Amundsen and Mr. Lincoln Ellsworth in charge, flying over the North Pole, 1926

The "Norge" carried as her medical equipment a 'Tabloid' Medical Outfit, a specially-fitted aeronautical case for aerial flight.

Meanwhile, Lieutenant-Commander Richard Evelyn Byrd had forestalled Ellsworth and Amundsen in a flight to the North Pole. In 1925, he had his first experience in the north when he commanded the aviation unit of the MacMillan Polar Expedition. In the following year he took off from Spitzbergen a few days before Amundsen and Ellsworth started. With Floyd Bennett as his pilot, he flew to the Pole and back in fifteen and a half hours. This feat made Lieutenant-Commander Byrd the first man to fly over the North Pole. He also carried a 'Tabloid' Equipment in a special aeronautical case.

Byrd

REAR-ADMIRAL BYRD—FIRST AEROPLANE FLIGHT TO THE SOUTH POLE

Rear-Admiral Byrd is the only airman who has flown over both North and South Poles. His machine is here seen flying through the passage of Liv's Glacier en route to the South Pole

Byrd's greatest glory was still to come. For his Polar flight, the Navy promoted him to the rank of Commander, and President Coolidge presented him with the Hubbard Gold Medal "for valor in exploration." He was also awarded the Congressional Medal of Honor, the D.S.M., the Flying Cross and 22 citations from the Navy Department. Then he flew from New York to the coast of France in 42 hours, with Bert Acosta and Bernt Balchen. This has been entirely eclipsed by his historic achievements in the Antarctic.

Byrd's Antarctic Expedition was the most sumptuously equipped that has ever been known. Commander Byrd had three vessels and three aeroplanes. He established his Base Camp in the Bay of Whales, a Camp known the world over as "Little America." His organisation was flawless. He took his time and made his preparations in a most methodical fashion. He had made provision against every possible contingency. The living quarters, the houses and warehouses, which he set up at "Little America," were shipped out in sections. He had the most up-to-date scientific instruments and complete photographic apparatus.

"Little America"

The medical supplies furnished by Burroughs Wellcome & Co. were comprehensive and included a large variety of 'Tabloid' Medicaments, 'Tabloid' Bandages and Dressings, a number of 'Tabloid' First-Aid Kits and Medicine Cases of different sizes, some for use at the base, and others for separate exploring parties. A small pharmacy, the farthest south in the world, was fitted up at "Little America," which Byrd named the "Wellcome Dispensary" in honour of the President of Burroughs Wellcome & Co. (U.S.A.) Inc. At this Farthest South Dispensary, under the supervision of the medical officer, medicines were dispensed and injuries treated. The health of the entire party was maintained at a high level.

The most Southerly Dispensary

Finally, on November 28, 1929, Commander Byrd, with Bernt Balchen and Harold June at the controls and McKinley as camera operator, took off and reached the high Polar Plateau, flying up the dangerous Liv Glacier to an elevation of 12,000 feet. At 1.14 p.m. Greenwich time, on November 29, he flew over the South Pole, made a complete circuit and returned to his base, without the slightest discomfort. Thus, 'Tabloid' Equipments have a unique record. They were first at the North Pole with Peary, second with Byrd, and third with Amundsen and Ellsworth, as well as first at the South Pole with Amundsen, second with Scott and third with Byrd. Among other things, Byrd

Part of the 'TABLOID' MEDICAL EQUIPMENT supplied to the Byrd Antarctic Expedition

discovered a new mountainous region which he

Radio communication maintained

claimed for the United States under the name of Marie Byrd Land. Throughout these entire expeditions, as on his present one, he was in touch with the United States by radio. Commander Byrd already had received nearly all the medals and degrees that could be conferred upon him. But, for this exploit, he was promoted to Rear-Admiral in the United States Navy.

When the time came for leaving "Little America," the condition of the ice pack made haste imperative, and much equipment was left behind. But when the second Byrd Antarctic Expedition returned to "Little America" at the end of 1933, the houses, aeroplanes and equipment were found in good condition. For this second Expedition, 'Tabloid' medical supplies were again selected—an expression of Rear-Admiral Byrd's faith in their dependability and efficiency, which is expressed in the report appearing upon the facing page.

BYRD ANTARCTIC EXPEDITION

New York
Executive Offices
RICHARD G. BROPHY
Business Manager

Address Reply:
Suite 340
BILTMORE HOTEL
New York

September 27, 1928.

Burroughs Wellcome & Co. (U.S.A.) Inc.,
9 & 11 East 41st Street,
New York, N. Y.

Gentlemen :

The 'Tabloid' Medicine Cases for the airplanes and the medical supplies for the expedition which you were commissioned to furnish as the official medical equipment for the Antarctic Expedition have been received.

Our medical officers have assured me that the needs of the expedition have been more than adequately anticipated. I have personally examined the medical supplies with a great deal of satisfaction.

The 'Tabloid' First-Aid and Medical Equipments which are to serve as the medical units for the airplanes of the expedition have received my special attention. As always these medical outfits are the last word in compactness and portability.

I carried 'Tabloid' Medical Equipments on the exploration flight in the Arctic, over the North Pole and also on my Trans-Atlantic Flight. In each instance the medical equipment has served with great efficiency and I consider it indispensable in exploration work. From personal experience I know that your medicinal preparations absolutely live up to their established universal reputation for exceptional purity, accuracy and reliability, and possess unusual keeping qualities.

Sincerely yours,

R E Byrd

R. E. Byrd/4

(RICHARD EVELYN BYRD, COMMANDER)

A SECTION OF THE WELLCOME DISPENSARY AT "LITTLE AMERICA"

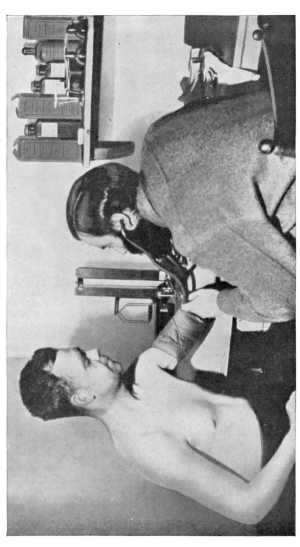

Examination of a patient at the Wellcome Dispensary, so named "in appreciation of the assistance you have given to my Expedition" (*radio message from Rear-Admiral Byrd to Sir Henry Wellcome*). Rear-Admiral Byrd has relied on 'Tabloid' Medical Outfits for all his Expeditions. This Dispensary, the most Southern in the world, is equipped with 'Wellcome' Chemicals and other Burroughs Wellcome & Co. products

An outstanding figure in the field of Polar exploration is George Hubert Wilkins. One of the most modest and unassuming of men, he is also one of the most gallant and capable. Many interesting anecdotes are told by his friends how Wilkins has frequently done valuable things for which others **Wilkins** got the credit. Whenever such episodes occurred, he has taken it with a grin and humorously allowed others to accept the praise that was due to him. But merit, like murder, will out. Wilkins is known the world over as a brave and brilliant man.

He was born in Australia and learned to fly as early as 1910. In 1913, he joined the Canadian Arctic Expedition, which was commanded by Vilhjalmur Stefansson. Eventually, he became second in command and held the position until 1917. In that year he went to the front, joined the Australian Flying Corps as photographer, and before the end of the war was chief in command of the Photographic Unit. He was decorated for bravery. Wilkins appalled some of his fellow officers because he took many pictures with the utmost sangfroid under the hottest kinds of bombardments.

In 1920-21, Wilkins was second in command of the British Imperial Antarctic Expedition, and later sailed on the Shackleton-Rowett party as naturalist. A couple of years later, he went back to his own country and made an exploration of tropical Australia for the British Museum, bringing back many priceless specimens and much information. In 1927, he attempted his first flying in the Arctic. Starting off from Point Barrow, he flew 530 miles north-west and made an early survey of a great stretch of unexplored country. The following year he beat the record established by Amundsen and Ellsworth, flying from Point Barrow to Spitzbergen in $20\frac{1}{2}$ hours. The same trip, in the opposite direction, had taken Ellsworth and Amundsen 72 hours. However, they were flying in a dirigible, whereas Wilkins was in a plane. For this exploit he was knighted by King George.

On all his expeditions, including his original and daring attempt to reach the North Pole in the submarine "Nautilus," Sir George Hubert Wilkins has relied for medical supplies solely on 'Tabloid' Medical Equipment.

RELIC 'TABLOID' MEDICINE CASES—POLAR EXPLORATION

1—Scottish National Antarctic Medicine Case. 2—Chest used during three years' exploration by the Jackson-Harmsworth Arctic Expedition. 3—A duplicate of the Chest carried by the Duke of the Abruzzi's Polar Expedition. 4—Part of the complete Medical Equipment supplied by Burroughs Wellcome & Co. for the National Antarctic Expedition, 1901. 5—Andrée, on his historical attempt to reach the North Pole by balloon, carried a Case of this design. 6—Medicine Case used by Wellman on his attempt to reach the North Pole in an airship. 7—Carried on the journey to the summit of Mount Erebus, and during the "Farthest South" journey, British Antarctic Expedition, 1907/9. 8—Case carried by the party which reached the South Magnetic Pole, British Antarctic Expedition, 1907/9. 9—Chest which formed part of Peary's equipment on his historic discovery of the North Pole. 10—Belt supplied to Nansen for journey "Farthest North."

PIONEERS OF AIR TRAVEL

THERE is no place where medical equipment that is both reliable and compact to the last degree is more necessary than in the air. Anybody can realise that these qualities are absolutely essential. When aerial travel became an accomplished fact, Burroughs Wellcome & Co., as we have seen, had already for some 30 years been the acknowledged specialists in light and portable outfits. With the birth of aviation, 'Tabloid' Cases and their contents were especially adapted to the peculiar requirements of aviators. Of 'Tabloid' First-Aid, the journal *Aeronautics* reported :—

"Every item in the internal fitting of an aeroplane should be as light, compact and efficient as it is possible to make it. This principle of selection has been applied by Messrs. Burroughs Wellcome & Co. to 'Tabloid' First-Aid.

"Since these products combine lightness, efficiency and compactness, it is not surprising to find them on board modern aircraft and in use by the famous aviators who are winning fresh laurels and making fresh records day by day in the world of flight.

"The same keen spirit of criticism and of selection which produced wondrous effects in engineering has been brought to bear upon the problems of medical supplies, and as a result 'Tabloid' medicaments have been evolved to meet the modern requirements of emergency first-aid. They bear the same relation to the cumbrous, old-fashioned medical and surgical equipments as does the modern, fast-flying aeroplane to the balloon."

Thus it came about that Burroughs Wellcome & Co. outfits, first at the North Pole and first at the South Pole, were also first in the air. All the men whose names live as pioneers in the conquest of the ether have carried 'Tabloid' First-Aid Equipments. For instance,

BLÉRIOT—FIRST CROSS-CHANNEL FLIGHT
M. Louis Blériot approaching the English Coast on the morning of
July 25, 1909

BRITISH AIRSHIP R 34—FIRST RETURN FLIGHT ACROSS
THE ATLANTIC
The airship is shown flying over New York City

Louis Blériot who upheld the pride of France by being the first to fly across the English Channel on July 25, 1909. Here is his report:—

> "I find 'Tabloid' First-Aid Outfits most useful, and I have seen them in the hands of many of my friends, who, like me, think that no sportsman can run the risk of being without one."

(LOUIS BLÉRIOT)

Blériot's Cross-Channel exploit was soon duplicated by his countryman, Henri Farman, in a hydroplane. Farman, who was an enthusiast about Esperanto, made his comment on the 'Tabloid' First-Aid in that language :—

> "Mi trovas estas tre necesa ke ĉiu flugisto havas kun li via 'TABLOID' UNUA-HELPO kaj konas ESPERANTO, per tioi ili ĉiuj iros for. Feliĉe, mi povas diri ke gis nun, neniam m, havis gravan okazon, sed ofte, laborante sur la diversaj aparatoj, mi malbonigis min kaj mi estis tre kontenta trovi la 'TABLOID' EKIPAJO, kiu ŝparas multekostan tempon."

(HENRI FARMAN)

The translation is as follows :—

> "I find it very necessary for every aviator to have with him one of your 'Tabloid' First-Aid Cases, and to know Esperanto. With these two he can go anywhere.

> "Fortunately, I can say that I have not yet had a serious accident, but working on the various apparatus, I have hurt myself several times, and was then glad to use the 'Tabloid' Case, which saves much valuable time."

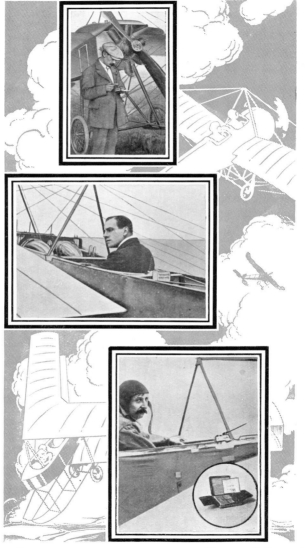

SOME PIONEER AVIATORS WHO CARRIED 'TABLOID' FIRST-AID

1. Védrines   2. Grahame-White   3. Blériot

Amongst the pioneers of aviation in England was an American, S. F. Cody. He had done important work for the British War Office in connexion with man-lifting kites, and was thus familiar with some of the problems of the air when he constructed and flew an aeroplane of his own design. He won the British Empire Michelin Trophy, 1910, and always carried 'Tabloid' First-Aid as his medical equipment.

THE FIRST AIR MAIL

The first birdman to deliver letters by aeroplane was the Frenchman, Jules Védrines. He won the Paris to Madrid race in 1911. Furthermore, in crossing the Pyrenees, Védrines had to rise to a height of more than 6000 feet, a record height at that time. To make his task more dangerous still, while in mid-air he was attacked by an eagle. In January, 1912, Védrines broke another world's record by attaining a speed of 105 miles an hour. He was also equipped by Burroughs Wellcome & Co. with a 'Tabloid' Pocket Outfit. His report was :—

"Je considère votre Premier-Secours 'Tabloid' comme très utile. Son peu de volume en fait modèle d'une extrême commodité."

(JULES VÉDRINES)

Keith-Davies, an English pioneer aviator, was the first man to fly in India, and, therefore, the first airman to carry 'Tabloid' First-Aid in that Empire.

Henri Pécquet, another of the gallant band of French pioneer aviators, established an Indian record in 1911. He carried a bag of mail in India all the way from Allahabad across the Jumna to Naini. This was the first aerial mail recognised by the Government of India. He, too, carried 'Tabloid' First-Aid, and wrote :—

"J'ai toujours emporté avec moi l'équipement Premier-Secours 'Tabloid,' et puis vous confirmer qu'il m'a toujours été de très grande utilité aux petits accidents que j'ai eus."

(HENRI PÉCQUET)

Among the heroes of the early days of aviation was Naval Lieutenant Jean Conneau. Flying under the name of André Beaumont, he won the European Circuit Race, also the London *Daily Mail* $50,000 prize for the circuit of Britain. He always had with him a 'Tabloid' First-Aid, of which he wrote:—

> "Grâce à sa légèreté et son format, la petite bôite 'Tabloid' First Aid se recommande spécialement aux aviateurs."

(LIEUT. JEAN CONNEAU)

There is hardly any end to the list of celebrated aviators who have carried these 'Tabloid' equipments. For instance, McCurdy, Sopwith, Tabuteau, Garros, Hubert Latham and many others. Here is what Latham said:—

> "Je tiens à vous dire combien m'a été utile votre trousse de Premier-Secours 'Tabloid.'
>
> "Elle est si peu volumineuse que je n'hesite jamais a l'emporter en aeroplane, et elle m'a rendu service plusieurs fois, surtout dans les meetings d'aviation où un pansement rapide est souvent nécessaire. Bien à vous."

(HUBERT LATHAM)

And Louis Paulhan, after he had won the *Daily Mail's* $50,000 for the first flight from London to Manchester, in 1910, flying through the night against Claude Grahame-White, reported as follows:—

> "Je profite de cette occasion pour vous exprimer le plaisir que j'ai eu de porter avec moi durant le vol que j'ai fait de Londres à Manchester une trousse Premier-Secours 'Tabloid.'

(L. PAULHAN)

The first air-mail in America was carried by Earle Ovington. This pioneer work was done under the personal supervision of Frank Hitchcock, who was then Postmaster-General. On one occasion, Postmaster-General Hitchcock accompanied Mr. Ovington on a mail flight. 'Tabloid' First-Aid Equipments were used on all these journeys.

> "I have looked the ('Tabloid') outfits over carefully and wish to compliment you upon the wonderful compactness and efficiency of your product. I feel decidedly more comfortable because I know I have your little outfits along with me to administer to my aid when necessity arises."

Earle L. Ovington

(EARLE L. OVINGTON)

POST-WAR PIONEER FLIGHTS

The most brilliant era of aviation really began after the War and it is worth remembering that every dirigible, every aeroplane, the pioneer planes which either attempted or accomplished a trans-atlantic, trans-Pacific or other long distance flight, were fitted out with 'Tabloid' First-Aid Equipment.

The establishing of post-war records began with Americans. The first man to cross the Atlantic from America to Great Britain in a heavier-than-air machine was Commander Read of the U.S. Navy with Seaplane NC.C 4. However, that was not a non-stop flight. It was a test of planning rather than of speed. Commander Read took off on May 16, went by way of the Azores and Lisbon, and landed on English soil May 31, 1919. *Across the Atlantic* The United States Navy authorities had given the most careful attention to the equipment of this attempt. 'Tabloid' Compressed Dressings and other Burroughs Wellcome & Co. First-Aid accessories were selected in order to assure the utmost economy of weight and space.

But it was the British Union Jack that flew with the first non-stop flight from the New World to the Old. That was on June 14–15, 1919, when Captain John Alcock and Lieutenant Brown hopped from

'TABLOID' FIRST-AID EQUIPMENTS
Carried by the pioneers of Transatlantic and Australian Flights
1. Alcock   2. Hawker   3. Ross Smith

Newfoundland to Ireland in a Vickers-Vimy machine. They did it in 16 hours and 12 minutes, won themselves a $50,000 prize from the London *Daily Mail* and also a knighthood for each.

"Part of the equipment of the Vickers-Vimy machine in which I crossed the Atlantic consisted of a 'Tabloid' First-Aid Case. It is the only possible medical outfit for an aviator."

J. Alcock

(J. ALCOCK)

The achievement of Alcock and Brown made up to England for the gallant failure of Commander Grieve and H. G. Hawker. Just at about the time that the American, Commander Read, was proceeding from New York to England, Grieve and Hawker took off from Newfoundland. When they had gone 1900 miles they crashed. Fortunately, the accident was not fatal. There was a sensational rescue at sea and both Commander Grieve and Mr. Hawker were saved. They also carried with them a 'Tabloid' First-Aid Equipment, of which Mr. Hawker wrote :—

"It is an admirable and wonderfully compact and light case and very useful in emergencies."

Yours faithfully

(H. G. HAWKER)

'TABLOID' CASE carried on First Flight round the World

America then won the laurels for the first round-the-world flight. This was just as much an achievement of organisation as of clever navigation and piloting. Lieutenant Lowell H. Smith and his companions, in four planes, made a triumphant circuit of the globe. They took their time about it and did not attempt any record. The sole medical equipment

Round the world

ROSS SMITH—FIRST ENGLAND TO AUSTRALIA FLIGHT
Capt. Sir Ross Smith's aeroplane on the concluding stage of his pioneer
flight over a dozen countries, November 12 to December 10, 1919

COBHAM—FIRST RETURN FLIGHT ENGLAND TO AUSTRALIA
Sir Alan Cobham landing on the Thames in front of the British Houses
of Parliament at the conclusion of his pioneer flight, October, 1926

on each of these four planes was a 'Tabloid' Medicine Chest. One of these, autographed by the successful birdmen, was presented to Burroughs Wellcome & Co. as a souvenir of the voyage. With it was enclosed a most favourable official report.

The first direct transatlantic flight by airship was accomplished by the British Government Airship R 34, which, leaving East Fortune, Scotland, on July 2, 1919, reached New York in $4\frac{1}{2}$ days, after a journey of 3500 miles. Subsequently, the R 34 returned by a more southerly route of 4000 miles. She was commanded by Major Scott, and carried Brigadier-General Maitland, Director of the Airship Department, British Admiralty, and other officers, in addition to the crew.

The airship, on her historic flight, carried a 'Tabloid' Medical and First-Aid Equipment.

Capt. Ross Smith, who flew from Hounslow, near London, to Port Darwin, Australia, and on to Melbourne (being afterwards knighted by King George V), was equipped with a 'Tabloid' Outfit. The Case selected by him was 'Tabloid' First-Aid, No. 715, specially fitted to supply the needs of his great adventure.

England to
Australia

Referring to this equipment, Capt. Sir Ross Smith reported :—

"It is a complete outfit for emergencies, but so compact that it takes up no material space on the machine."

Ross Smith Capt.
A.F.C.

(CAPT. ROSS SMITH, A.F.C.)

One memorable flight was that of Sir Alan Cobham, from England to Australia and back. He started in June and was back in October. Of course, his record has since been broken for speed. But it must be remembered that Cobham was a pioneer when he did it. Aeroplanes have been vastly improved in the subsequent years; navigating instruments, radio direction-finders and a host of appliances have been developed since 1926. So much the more credit is due to Cobham. His journey was really one of exploration and its success was due to fine organisation. He took with him a 'Tabloid' First-Aid Outfit when he left, and before he took off from Sydney, on his return voyage, the Australian house of Burroughs Wellcome & Co. replenished his outfit. They received a report from this gallant flier, in which he confirmed the experience of all his peers with 'Tabloid' Equipment.

At the conclusion of this flight Cobham alighted on the river Thames, alongside the British Houses of Parliament.

Subsequently, Cobham made a number of pioneer survey flights, including one of **20,000** miles round Africa and another across Central Africa. He wrote on his return :—

> "I write to tell you how very glad we were on the occasion of our flight to Lake Kivu and back, we had one of your 'Tabloid' First-Aid Cases on board . . . . my crew could hardly avoid cuts, knocks and abrasions, but a ready access to the 'Tabloid' Case made it possible for all these to be put right on the spot."

(SIR ALAN COBHAM)

There is no need to expatiate here upon the career of the aviator who ranks a supreme first in American affections. Since Charles A. Lindbergh made history by winging with mathematical precision from Curtiss Field, N.Y., to Le Bourget, France, in only 21 hours 20 minutes' flying time, several of his successors have made considerably greater non-stop distance records. But Colonel Lindbergh's exploit today is outstanding in the popular memory and the popular imagination.

He accomplished that pioneer solo flight with such apparent ease because he had made so many meticulously careful preparations. On that occasion, as on others, Colonel Lindbergh was furnished with a 'Tabloid' First-Aid Outfit.

Epilogue

We have seen the importance of the medical aspect in exploration. Little imagination is needed to envisage the place of the Burroughs Wellcome Medical Kits in wars. A ponderous tome would be needed to tell the long tragic stories of war and the art of healing—or the lack of the art of healing in the past. Think what horrors might have been averted in the wars of the 19th century if the 'Tabloid' medicaments had been available. Take, for instance, the Crimean affair. The phase of that campaign, which stirred Florence Nightingale into such dynamic activity, was not so much the carnage as the sufferings caused by the deficiency of healing equipment.

For over 40 years the Burroughs Wellcome & Co. outfits have been employed in the medical equipment of military expeditions. Their usefulness was demonstrated during the last British Military Expedition in Ashanti, as is shown by the official Government report made by the Chief Medical Officer of the Expedition on the 'Tabloid' Medical Equipment supplied by Burroughs Wellcome & Co. :—

"The supply of medicines, both as to quality and quantity, left nothing to be desired. There was no scarcity of anything. The 'Tabloid' medicines were found to be most convenient and of excellent quality. To be able to take out at once the required dose of any medicine, without having to weigh or measure it, is a convenience that cannot be expressed in words. Time is saved to an extent that can hardly be realised, and so is space, for a fitted dispensary, or even a dispensary table, is unnecessary. The quality of medicines was so good that no other should be taken into the field. The cases supplied are almost ideal ones for the Government. They are light, yet strong, and the arrangement of the materials and medicines is as nearly perfect as possible."

It is instructive to compare the experience of this Expedition with that of the Wolseley Ashanti Expedition of 1873, fitted out according to old-time methods. The suffering and loss of life were then terrible, for want of suitable medical equipments.

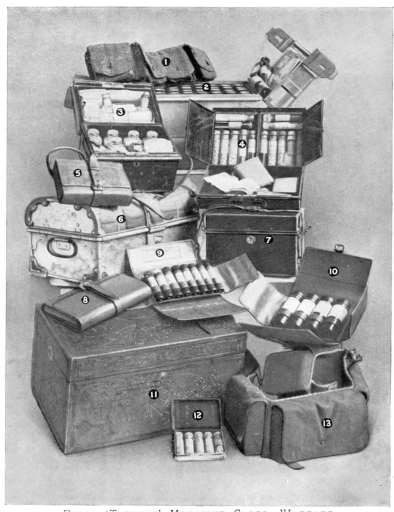

RELIC 'TABLOID' MEDICINE CASES—WARFARE

1—One of the Medicine Belts used during the Spanish-American War. 2—One of the Medicine Chests used in the Ashanti Campaign, 1895-6. 3—G. W. Steevens carried this equipment through many campaigns and journeys. 4—A relic of many battles and sieges, formerly the property of W. Maxwell, war correspondent. 5—One of the Cases supplied to the British Colonial contingents during the South African War. 6—Part of the Medical Equipment of Greece during the war with Turkey, 1897. 7—Duplicate of the Medical Equipment of Bennet Burleigh, war correspond-ent. 8—One of the portable Medicine Cases used on the Dongola Expedition. 9—A duplicate of the equipment used during the Anglo-Egyptian campaign in the Sudan. 10—A specially-designed Case carried by the C.I.V. in the South African War. 11—A specially-designed Chest, part of the medical equipment entirely supplied by Burroughs Wellcome & Co. for the Hospital Ship "Maine." 12—Pocket Medicine Case carried by General Viljoen throughout the South African War. 13—Medicine Belt used during the Benin Campaign.

The advantages of 'Tabloid' Medical Equipments were confirmed during Kitchener's Omdurman campaign. They proved their worth still further in the Boer War and in the Spanish-American imbroglio, on both the Cuban and Philippine fronts. They rendered incomparable service in the World War.

'Tabloid' Medical Equipments have subsequently been available to reduce to a minimum the horrors of sickness and wounds wherever men go forth with bullet, bayonet and bomb to destroy each other. In this connexion it is interesting to observe what the Special War Correspondent of *The Lancet*, a veteran of many campaigns, has to say :—

> "It affords me satisfaction to state that I have for some years dispensed—and have also seen administered by medical officers of both Naval and Military Services—Burroughs Wellcome & Co.'s 'Tabloid' preparations during the Sudan, Ashanti, Benin, South African and the more modern campaigns. I cannot refrain from expressing my opinions as to their distinct and marked superiority over the medicinal preparations of former days. They are far more portable, very acceptable so far as the palate is concerned, far less liable to absorb damp on service during rapid changes of climate, are always found exact as to their dose-weight and, what is of far more importance, retain their efficiency much longer than any other medicinal products I know of. The firm of Burroughs Wellcome & Co. are deservedly to be congratulated upon the marked scientific advance they have made in pharmaceutical reform."

For the benefit of American readers it might be well to explain that such a report from *The Lancet* is about as frequent as the appearance of Halley's Comet. It makes a fitting conclusion for this survey of adventure and achievement.

Sir Henry Morton Stanley, half a century ago, was troubled about his medical equipment. Burroughs Wellcome & Co. solved his difficulties. They have done the same for all subsequent explorers and travellers. The record speaks for itself.

The Burroughs Wellcome & Co. Exhibit, Chicago Exposition, 1934, West Front

Dioramas depicting pioneer exploits of exploration, etc.

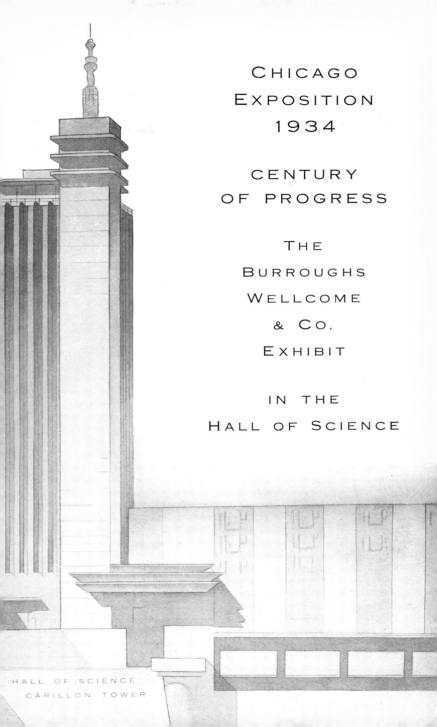

CHICAGO
EXPOSITION
1934

CENTURY
OF PROGRESS

THE
BURROUGHS
WELLCOME
& CO.
EXHIBIT

IN THE
HALL OF SCIENCE

HALL OF SCIENCE
CARILLON TOWER

THE BURROUGHS WELLCOME & CO. EXHIBIT, CHICAGO, 1934, SOUTH FRONT
'Tabloid' Emergency First-Aid and Medical Equipments, etc.

HISTORIC
'TABLOID' BRAND MEDICAL EQUIPMENTS

THE following extract from the "Official World's Fair Weekly," Chicago, July 22, 1933, describes the Burroughs Wellcome & Co. Exhibit of Historical Medical Equipments there shown. The present exhibit is enlarged by the addition of Historic Cases used in the 1933 Expeditions to Mount Everest by land and air:—

"Wherever the British Lion goes, there also goes the Unicorn, which represents Burroughs Wellcome & Co. You'll always find the two together, whether it is in the heart of Darkest Africa or at either of the two Poles. The same sun that never sets on the great Empire never sets on 'Tabloid' Medical Equipments either. Burroughs Wellcome & Co. are here at 'A Century of Progress' with one of the most thrilling displays that we have seen. Their dioramas whisk you away to all parts of the world so fast that it makes you dizzy. In one of them you are with Amundsen as he flew across the North Pole in 'The Norge'; in another you're trudging along over the eternal snows with Nansen as he leaves 'The Fram' and takes to the sledges. A moment later you are circling the world with the U.S. Army Fliers, who went round in the spring and summer of 1924. A quick change of temperature now, and you see Stanley on his first expedition into the black and dismal heart of Africa. You fly with Ross Smith from England to Australia—and back the other way with Sir Alan Cobham. A moment later you are away with Roy Chapman Andrews to the Gobi Desert and the high Himalayas. Finally, you go away with Byrd and Balchen in their 'plane through that narrow dangerous gorge that led to the South Pole. But what have Burroughs Wellcome & Co., those staid manufacturing chemists, to do with all this? Nothing, except that they went along, not in person, mind you, but represented in all these flights and expeditions and adventures by their famous 'Tabloid' Equipments."

TRADE MARK 'TABLOID' BRAND
MEDICINE CHESTS AND CASES

FOR TRAVELLERS, PLANTERS, MISSIONARIES, YACHTSMEN, SETTLERS, HUNTING AND EXPLORING EXPEDITIONS, CAMPS, ETC.

The BURROUGHS WELLCOME & Co. Exhibit at the Century of Progress Exposition, Chicago, 1934, includes photographs and relics of the 'TABLOID' Equipments carried by many famous explorers, travellers, missionaries, etc.

In the following pages will be found illustrations and short descriptions of outfits suitable for travellers and others who are, for short or long periods, cut off from the services of a medical man.

Those unable to visit the Century of Progress Exposition, Chicago, may order these outfits through their usual supply houses or inspect them at the Burroughs Wellcome & Co. Exhibition Rooms, 9–11 and 13–15, East Forty-first Street, New York City.

No. 117. 'TABLOID' BRAND MEDICINE POCKET-CASE

In Morocco, Brown or Green Seal or Crocodile Leather, Cowhide and in Pigskin. Contains *sixteen* $\frac{1}{2}$ oz. phials of 'Tabloid' Brand products. Also gusset pocket for dressings or papers, etc., etc.

No. 117 'Tabloid' Brand Medicine Pocket-Case
Measurements: $7\frac{1}{2} \times 4\frac{1}{2} \times 2\frac{5}{8}$ in.

No. 231. 'Tabloid' brand Medicine Case

An excellent Equipment for missionary, expeditionary or itinerant use.

Black Japanned Metal

Weight, about 8 lb.

No. 231. 'Tabloid' Brand Medicine Case
Measurements: $11 \times 8 \times 3\frac{5}{8}$ in

No. 250. 'Tabloid' brand Medicine Chest

Contains *thirty-six* stoppered bottles of 'Tabloid,' 'Soloid' and other Burroughs Wellcome & Co. fine products, minor surgical instruments, dressings, etc.

Japanned Sheet-iron   Weight, about 40 lb.

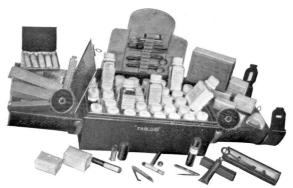

No. 250. 'Tabloid' Brand Medicine Chest
Measurements: $15\frac{3}{4} \times 10\frac{1}{2} \times 8\frac{1}{4}$ in.

No. 251. 'Tabloid' brand Medicine Chest

Contains *forty* $3\frac{1}{2}$ oz. feather-weight bottles of 'TABLOID,' 'SOLOID' and other Burroughs Wellcome & Co. fine products. In other respects it is fitted in the same way as the No. 250 Chest. The ideal expeditionary outfit when lightness and completeness of equipment are essential.

Aluminium   Weight, about 27 lb.

No. 251. 'Tabloid' Brand Medicine Chest
Measurements: $15 \times 10\frac{1}{4} \times 8\frac{1}{2}$ in.

No. 254. 'Tabloid' brand Medicine Chest
("The Indian")

Contains *sixteen* $1\frac{3}{4}$ oz. glass-stoppered bottles and *six* 4 dr. phials of 'TABLOID' and 'SOLOID' Brand products, instruments and tray carrying sundry dressings, etc. Ideal for missionary, expeditionary or station use when smaller equipments than No. 250 and No. 251 are required.

Black Japanned Metal

Weight, about 12 lb.

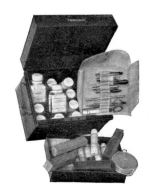

No. 254. 'Tabloid' Brand Medicine Chest
("The Indian")
Measurements: $9 \times 6\frac{3}{4} \times 6\frac{1}{4}$ in.

No. 258. 'Tabloid' brand Medicine Case
("The Settler's")

Compact and useful for settlers' or travellers' use and for stations, farms, or camps in out-of-the-way places. A comprehensive equipment of 'Tabloid' Medicaments and Bandages, and 'Soloid' Antiseptics.

Black Japanned Metal

Weight, 5¼ lb.

No. 258. 'Tabloid' Brand Medicine Case
("The Settler's")
Measurements: 8¼ × 5¾ × 4⅝ in.

No. 260. 'Tabloid' brand Medicine Case
("The Safari")

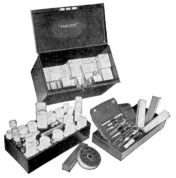

No. 260. 'Tabloid' Brand Medicine Case
("The Safari")
Measurements: 9¾ × 7⅞ × 5½ in.

Specially designed for the medical equipment of hunting expeditions and camps or for small expeditionary parties. Contains 'Tabloid' Medicaments, 'Soloid' Antiseptics, 'Tabloid' Bandages and Dressings, minor surgical instruments, etc.

Black Japanned Metal

THE BURROUGHS WELLCOME & CO. EXHIBIT, HALL OF SCIENCE, CHICAGO EXPOSITION, 1934
NORTH FRONT. 'Tabloid' Compressed Medicaments, etc.

PIONEER WORK

THE Burroughs Wellcome & Co. Exhibit at Chicago, 1934, is designed to illustrate pioneer work in research, and in the production of fine chemical and pharmaceutical products, medical equipments, etc.

The history of the firm is rich in pioneer achievements in the realm of science allied to industry.

Succeeding to the sole proprietorship of the business of Brockedon, who, in 1842, originated compressed medicines in the shape of bi-convex discs, issued under the designation of "Compressed Pills," Burroughs Wellcome & Co. have revolutionised the preparation of compressed products, which are issued chiefly under the trade mark brand 'TABLOID.' Compressed products

In the EXPERIMENTAL RESEARCH LABORATORIES at the Wellcome Chemical and Galenical Works and Laboratories, New York, research work is continually being carried out, and some of the results are shown in a group of cases occupying the central position in the exhibit.

One section is devoted to the purely scientific aspects of the work of the Laboratories.

Half of one case is a display of Synthetic Substances prepared in the organic Synthesis Laboratory. It comprises 130 substances in 15 exhibits arranged to show the type of reaction involved in the preparation of certain types of chemicals. Stages in the preparation of these chemicals are shown. Included in this display are the syntheses of 'Epinine,' 'Lodal' and Papaverine.

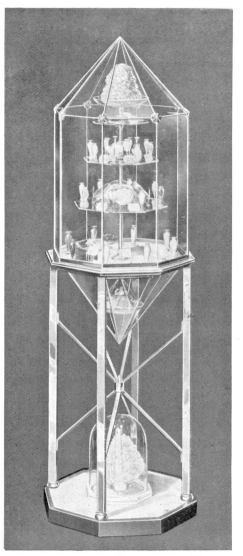

CRYSTAL SHOW-CASE

One of the five cases of original Burroughs Wellcome & Co. design. They represent crystals, and three contain crystals of exquisite form and beauty, symbolising the high standard of purity of 'WELLCOME' BRAND CHEMICALS.

The two others are devoted to exhibits of 'Tabloid' Hypodermic products and outfits, 'Agla' Syringes and Needles, 'Tabloid' Ophthalmic products and outfits, and 'Soloid' Test Cases.

PART OF THE BURROUGHS WELLCOME & CO. EXHIBIT
HALL OF SCIENCE, CHICAGO EXPOSITION, 1934

The other half of this case contains an exhibit from the Pharmacological Laboratory, illustrating the relationship of chemical constituents to physiological action of a series of amines which have been synthesised in the Laboratory. **Synthetic substances** Twelve of the amine substances are shown in specimen vases, with descriptive cards giving information as to the chemical structure and physiological properties of each substance. There are also illustrations of subjects displaying the characteristic deficiency symptoms of each of the vitamins in question.

In this case also are exhibits connected with an Ornithine research, including the parent protein, edestin arginine therefrom and ornithine derived from the arginine; also picrates and picralonates of the amine acids mentioned. Here also are displayed a highly-purified oleic acid, a highly-purified casein and calcium levulinate.

Charts illustrate researches in bio-physical chemistry and chemotherapy. Thirty-six reprints of scientific papers published, describing researches carried out in the Laboratories, are shown.

Numerous products, the existence or exceptional purity of which is due to pioneer research work in the Burroughs Wellcome & Co. Experimental Laboratories in London or New York, are shown in the exhibit. In the few pages available, however, **Typical pioneer products** it is possible to refer only to the few typical examples mentioned above and to 'DEXIN' High Dextrin Carbohydrate, which provides palatable, easily-digested carbohydrate for modifying cows' milk in infant feeding and for addition to the diet of convalescents or adults subject to intestinal disturbances of a fermentative character.

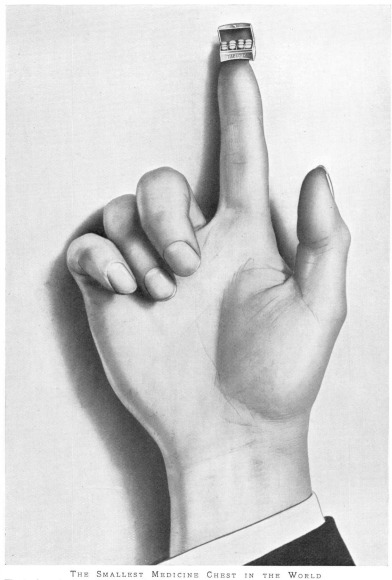

THE SMALLEST MEDICINE CHEST IN THE WORLD

The twelve minute medicine chest bottles with which this tiny gold Medicine Chest is fitted are capable of containing a supply of 'Tabloid' Brand Medicaments that would represent in therapeutic value the bulky medicines with which the average medicine chest is usually equipped. A replica of this Chest, in 18-carat gold, was part of the equipment of the Doll's House presented to Her Majesty Queen Mary of Great Britain.

_{TRADE}
_{MARK} # 'TABLOID' _{BRAND}

EMERGENCY

FIRST-AID

FOR ALL CLIMATES

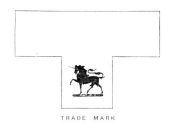

TRADE MARK

FOR THE

HOME	GARAGE
MINE	AUTOMOBILE
FACTORY	YACHT
LABORATORY	MOTOR BOAT
LAUNDRY	CAMP
GARDEN	AIRPLANE

FIRST-AID ON THE ROAD
'TABLOID' FIRST-AID, No. 716, in use after a Motor Accident
(see page 121*)*

FIRST-AID IN THE HOME
'TABLOID' FIRST-AID, No. 715, immediately available after an
Accident in the Garden

FIRST-AID IN EMERGENCIES

MOST people are confronted, sooner or later, with the necessity of applying First-Aid. The accident may be quite trivial **Are you prepared for accidents?** or it may be a matter of life or death. The only point on which we may count is that its advent will be sudden and unexpected.

The question which occurs to every thoughtful person is—

"How will I be equipped in knowledge and appliances to deal effectively with accidental injuries should they occur when medical aid is not available immediately or cannot be obtained for hours or, in some remote parts, for days?"

Burroughs Wellcome & Co., as a result of their unique experience in supplying most of the historic Expeditions of the 19th century and the 20th century with Medical Equipments, stand in an unrivalled position as suppliers of First-Aid Equipment **'Tabloid' First-Aid** for any and every purpose. These outfits are intended only for emergency use and must not be employed to rob the patient of qualified medical aid. First-aid is, as its name implies, a temporary measure to ensure the greatest comfort and safety until the doctor or surgeon arrives.

'TABLOID' FIRST-AID, particularly the non-technical outfits, is so simple that in many instances it can be applied effectively by an inexperienced amateur should the emergency demand immediate action.

The following pages illustrate the wide range of equipment available.

FIRST-AID ON VACATION

ON VACATION you frequently visit or reach in your travels by yacht, car or plane, places remote from medical aid.

Your camp or caravan will rest far from town or even village.
In camp It is under such circumstances that accidents may **or caravan** happen which, unless reliable first-aid materials are available, may mar or even ruin the holiday.

Trifling cuts, burns, sprains, etc., may develop into serious matters unless they receive immediate first-aid attention, and the consequences of more serious injuries can be minimised if proper first-aid is applied until it is possible for them to receive medical attention.

At sea, particularly on board a sailing or motor yacht, the provision of a first-aid outfit is essential. Ropes may abrade the skin or even cut through the flesh; there may be a slip on deck **On board** resulting in bruises or perhaps a sprained ankle; there **yacht** may be cuts or contusions from sharp or blunt instruments, burns or scalds from the engine or cooking range. These and other mishaps can be dealt with, until, if necessary, medical aid is obtained, when there is a 'Tabloid' First-Aid outfit on board.

There are 'Tabloid' First-Aid Kits to suit every need of the vacation, wherever or however it is spent. If in doubt as to which equipment to take, the expert advice of Burroughs Wellcome & Co. is always available.

There are pocket-kits, such as No. 714, or outfits suitable for the yacht cabin, or for caravan or camp, such as No. 716 *(page* 121*)* and No. 718 *(page* 122*)*.

No. 714. 'Tabloid' First-Aid
("Pocket Kit")

Contains 'Tabloid' Bandage and Boric Compress, 'Vaporole' Iodine Applicator, 'Vaporole' Aromatic Ammonia, 'Borofax' Brand Boric Acid Ointment, 'Carofax' Brand Solidified Carron Oil and adhesive plaster.

Blue and Gilt
Enamelled Metal

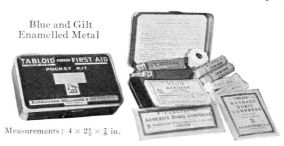

Measurements: $4 \times 2\frac{1}{2} \times \frac{7}{8}$ in.

Accidents in Camp

When preparing for camping, hunting, hiking or fishing trips, choose your first-aid outfit as carefully as the rest of your equipment. The main thing to keep in mind is the ideal of "A place for everything and everything in its place." **Go light but right** You should carry a proper assortment of just those bandages, dressings and first-aid materials which are most likely to be required, packed in the neatest, most convenient and most compact manner.

'Tabloid' First-Aid fills these requirements in every particular. So many and so various are the sizes and styles in which these equipments are issued, that it is possible to satisfy every individual need. The boy scout or the out-of-doors man wanting an outfit to carry on a one-day hike, **Scope of 'Tabloid' First-Aid** or a party intending to remain in the wilds for months at a time, will find exactly what is required in the series of 'Tabloid' Equipments.

When provided with a 'Tabloid' First-Aid you know that if need arises you will find the right thing just when you want it.

FIRST-AID IN THE HOME

'Tabloid' First-Aid handy for little accidents in the home.

A moment's attention may prevent serious consequences.

TRADE MARK 'TABLOID' BRAND FIRST-AID No. 720 ("S.K. KIT")

Measurements: $8\frac{1}{2} \times 7\frac{3}{4} \times 2\frac{1}{2}$ in.

FIRST-AID IN THE HOUSE

Children are always getting into mischief, but the wise mother does not worry when they come running to her with their cuts and bruises. Tenderly and skilfully she applies the necessary ointment or dressing, kept scrupulously clean and ready for use in the neat domestic 'TABLOID' FIRST-AID, NO. 720.

First-aid work with 'Tabloid' Bandages and Dressings provides a useful object lesson for all the family, and the value of prompt and efficient treatment with reliable materials is soon perceived. Make-shift bandages and dressings find no place in the well-appointed household. They may seem cheap—at first sight—but they are clumsy and inconvenient and always cause delay when wanted in a hurry.

Aids to efficient treatment

'TABLOID' BRAND FIRST-AID, NO. 720, contains an excellent assortment of first-aid dressings and accessories. Taking up little room, it is never in the way, but is always ready for use.

FIRST-AID

IN THE FACTORY OR PLANT

The various protective measures adopted in modern, well-equipped factories have greatly reduced the number of accidents, but mishaps still occur in spite of the most elaborate precautions. It therefore becomes the duty of all who are placed in positions of authority and responsibility in the industrial world to provide adequate first-aid facilities. A reliable service of this nature is a sound business proposition and saves thousands of dollars as well as lives and limbs. Risks of blood-poisoning and other serious consequences of industrial accidents are materially decreased, while time losses are reduced to a minimum.

A sound business proposition

The first-aid equipment, to be effective, must comprise materials of good quality, capable of being easily and promptly applied. Everything must be perfectly clean—a soiled dressing or bandage **Convenience and efficiency** may aggravate rather than alleviate an open wound and is positively dangerous. In the preparation of 'TABLOID' BRAND Bandages and Dressings materials of the best quality only are used. They are protected from contamination by being packed in special cartons which allow of the desired quantity being withdrawn without exposing the remainder. All waste is thus eliminated.

'TABLOID' BRAND FIRST-AID, designed to meet the peculiar requirements of every field, are described and illustrated below and on the facing page.

TRADE MARK 'TABLOID' BRAND FIRST-AID

No. 742

(For Factories and Workshops)

A reliable first-aid service is a necessity and such a service may readily be secured by installing this outfit in convenient positions, placing each one in charge of someone skilled in first-aid work. Accidents are apt to occur when least expected, and first-aid dressings are usually wanted in a hurry. It is then that the superlative service rendered by 'TABLOID' FIRST-AID, No. 742, is best appreciated.

Measurements: $8\frac{3}{4} \times 7 \times 4\frac{3}{4}$ in.

FIRST-AID IN THE FACTORY

When accidents happen, promptness in rendering first-aid saves money as well as lives and limbs.

The respective 'TABLOID' FIRST-AID are the last word in first-aid equipment for workshop, factory, department, etc.

TRADE MARK 'TABLOID' BRAND

FIRST-AID

NO. 744

Measurements: $13\frac{1}{4} \times 12 \times 2\frac{1}{4}$ in.

This model has been designed for use as a wall-case for workshops or factories where there are several or many departments each requiring separate equipment.

FIRST-AID IN THE WORKSHOP
'TABLOID' FIRST-AID, No. 744, in use after an Accident
at the Bench

FIRST-AID IN THE FACTORY
'TABLOID' FIRST-AID, No. 742, in use after an Accident
in the Boiler House

TRADE MARK 'TABLOID' BRAND FIRST-AID
NO. 728 ("MOTO KIT")

For use on motor fleets, buses, and commercial trucks. It will also be found quite suitable for use by railroad section gangs, small parties of engineers, mechanics engaged on outside work and similar groups of workers. Strongly constructed of heavy Japanned Metal it will withstand hard usage.

Measurements: $5\frac{1}{8} \times 3\frac{1}{8} \times 2\frac{1}{8}$ in.

TRADE MARK 'TABLOID' BRAND FIRST-AID
NO. 729
("MOTOR CYCLE KIT")

For State Police, Highway Patrols, Police Department Motor-Cycles

Measurements: $9 \times 5\frac{1}{4} \times 3$ in.

Designed to be installed on the rear fender of the motor-cycle. Can also be furnished for attaching to the rear carrier racks.

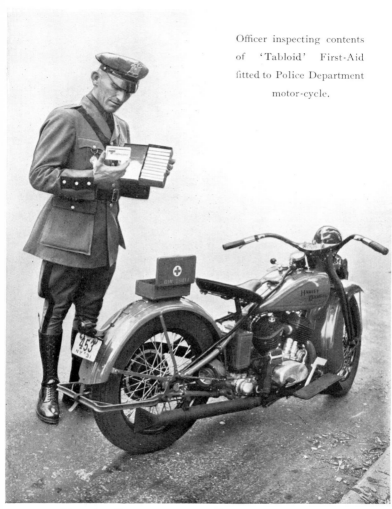

Officer inspecting contents of 'Tabloid' First-Aid fitted to Police Department motor-cycle.

MOBILE POLICE CARRY 'TABLOID' FIRST-AID

ACCIDENTS ON THE ROAD

Even the most cautious and skilful motorist is liable to be involved in an accident through circumstances beyond his control or by the carelessness of others. Such an accident may occur far from medical aid, and first-aid treatment may be essential if permanent injury or even death is to be avoided.

Be prepared to meet such an emergency by carrying a 'TABLOID' FIRST-AID Equipment and you will be able to act the Good Samaritan to those less careful than yourself. Accidents are apt to occur when least expected and first-aid dressings are usually wanted in a hurry. It is in such circumstances that the superlative service rendered by 'TABLOID' FIRST-AID is best appreciated, the Equipment being always ready and easily and promptly applied.

Automobilist's risks and responsibilities

'TABLOID' FIRST-AID ("Auto-Kit") has been specially designed for the automobilist, meeting his demand for a compact, portable outfit.

TRADE MARK 'TABLOID' BRAND FIRST-AID
NO. 716 ("AUTO-KIT")

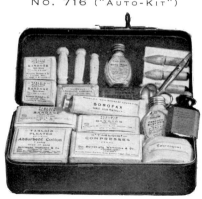

Measurements : $7\frac{5}{8} \times 4\frac{1}{4} \times 2$ in.   Weight, about $1\frac{1}{2}$ lb.

TRADE MARK 'TABLOID' BRAND FIRST-AID
NO. 718 ("SCHOOL KIT")

Specially designed for use in schools, public institutions, playgrounds and similar places. It is a wall type of Equipment having fasteners on the back to enable one to attach the case to the wall in a convenient position. The cover of the Case can be let down so as to serve as a tray for dispensing the contents.

Measurements: $8\frac{1}{2} \times 7\frac{3}{4} \times 2\frac{1}{2}$ in.

TRADE MARK 'TABLOID' BRAND FIRST-AID
NO. 721 ("SERVICE STATION KIT")

Designed for use in service stations and prepared and fitted in accordance with the specification of one of the largest Petroleum Corporations in the world. The Case is strongly constructed of heavy gauge Japanned Metal and is fitted with a carrying handle and wall hooks.

Measurements: $8\frac{1}{2} \times 7\frac{5}{8} \times 2\frac{3}{4}$ in.

^{TRADE MARK} 'TABLOID' BRAND FIRST-AID
("PAC-KITS")

Unit type First-Aid Outfits, containing first-aid materials of the highest quality in standardised units and multiples of that unit

The dressings are sealed, sterilised and so wrapped that they are dirt and dust proof

No. 750. 'TABLOID' FIRST-AID—10 UNITS
Measurements: $8 \times 5 \times 2\frac{7}{4}$ in.

No. 751. 'TABLOID' FIRST-AID—12 UNITS
Measurements: $9\frac{1}{4} \times 5 \times 2\frac{7}{4}$ in.

No. 752. 'TABLOID' FIRST-AID—16 UNITS
Measurements: $9 \times 6\frac{1}{2} \times 2\frac{7}{4}$ in.

No. 753. 'TABLOID' FIRST-AID—24 UNITS
Measurements: $9\frac{3}{8} \times 9\frac{1}{2} \times 2\frac{7}{4}$ in.

No. 754. 'TABLOID' FIRST-AID—36 UNITS
Measurements: $13\frac{3}{4} \times 9\frac{1}{2} \times 2\frac{7}{4}$ in.

No. 715 'Tabloid' brand First-Aid

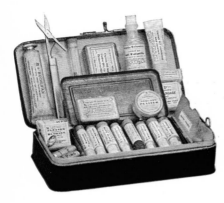

Contains 'Tabloid' Brand Bandages and Dressings, 'Vaporole' Iodine Applicator, 'Vaporole' Aromatic Ammonia, for use as "Smelling Salts," 'Borofax' Brand Boric Acid Ointment, sal volatile, 'Carofax' Brand Solidified Carron Oil, jaconet, plaster, protective skin, scissors, pins, etc., and eight tubes of 'Tabloid' and 'Soloid' Brand products.

Measurements: $7\frac{5}{8} \times 4\frac{1}{4} \times 2$ in.

No. 724 'Tabloid' brand First-Aid

("The Backwoodsman")

Contains 10 tubes of 'Tabloid' and 'Soloid' Brand products, 'Tabloid' Bandages, 'Tabloid' Absorbent Cotton, 'Vaporole' Iodine Applicator, 'Vaporole' Aromatic Ammonia, 'Carofax' Brand Solidified Carron Oil, 'Borofax' Brand Boric Acid Ointment, tourniquet, plaster, scissors, forceps, pins, etc.

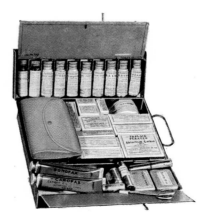

Measurements $8 \times 5\frac{1}{2} \times 2\frac{3}{8}$ in.

Iodine in First-Aid

THE immediate application of iodine to a cut, wound, abrasion, bite or sting as an antiseptic, counter-irritant and parasiticide is a very wise first-aid precaution. Solutions, however, undergo chemical change in ordinary containers and become very irritating.

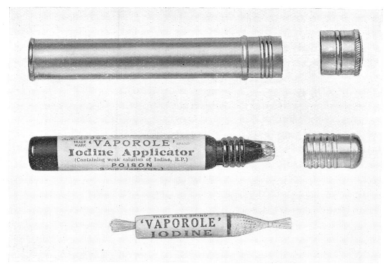

In 'Tabloid' First-Aid Outfits two special iodine containers are used—'VAPOROLE' IODINE APPLICATOR, a glass container with screw nozzle and cap fitting into an outer metal container, and 'VAPOROLE' Iodine, a fragile container surrounded by absorbent material enclosed in a silken sac. The applicator is used like a pencil; the 'Vaporole' Iodine is pinched between finger and thumb, the container breaks and converts the sac into an iodine swab.

The iodine is fresh and pure and either method of application is preferable to the use of a brush of doubtful cleanliness.

'Vaporole' Iodine Applicator or 'Vaporole' Iodine may be obtained of all Pharmacists and Druggists

FIRST-AID SNAKE-BITE OUTFIT

B. W. & CO.

As snake-bites occur most often on the hands and the lower portions of the body, an effective method of protection is to wear thick gloves, stout boots and leather leggings, whenever practicable. At night a lamp should be carried. In addition to these precautions, adequate means of dealing with a bite should always be instantly available. When an outfit can be procured, so compact and inexpensive as that shown in the illustration, everyone likely to incur the slightest danger should carry one constantly on the person.

The containing barrel is 3½ in. long and is fitted at one end with a long screw cap covering a lancet; at the other end, a small screw cap fits over a cavity in which is contained a supply of potassium permanganate crystals. Below is given a brief summary of the *first-aid* measures recommended for treating snake-bites; *but the aid of a surgeon should be obtained whenever practicable.*

If possible, the snake responsible for the bite should be killed and the head preserved so that it may be identified by the medical man.

SUMMARY OF TREATMENT

The first-aid treatment of snake-bite may be summarised as follows:—

1. Send for medical assistance.

2. Apply ligature above bite.

3. Lance the bite and surrounding tissues to allow escape of the venom.

4. Wash wound thoroughly with potassium permanganate solution or rub in the powdered solid.

5. Keep up circulation and breathing by stimulants or artificial respiration.

TRADE MARK 'BOROFAX' BRAND

BORIC ACID OINTMENT

AN IDEAL FIRST-AID DRESSING

ADMINISTER first-aid this way : after carefully washing the wound,

Reduced facsimile

cover it with a piece of lint, previously spread over with 'BOROFAX,' and bandage in the usual way. This keeps the wound clean and helps it to heal rapidly.

'BOROFAX' is better than ordinary boric acid ointment. It contains the same proportion of boric acid, but its base is more readily absorbed by the skin. Consequently, its action is more rapid. The tube packing makes it cleanly and convenient to use, and it never becomes rancid.

TRADE MARK 'CAROFAX' BRAND

SOLIDIFIED CARRON OIL

(with 2 per cent. Phenol)

THE convenient tube in which 'CAROFAX' Solidified Carron Oil is issued keeps the contents clean and wholesome, thus minimising the risk of contamination. 'CAROFAX' Carron Oil also contains 2 per cent. of Phenol, which exerts a distinct local anæsthetic action, making it peculiarly suitable for first-aid use. *(See also page* 142).

'Borofax' and 'Carofax' are obtainable from all Pharmacists and Druggists, in collapsible tubes of three sizes ; also in jars containing 16 oz.

EXTERIOR, HENRY VII'S CHAPEL
WESTMINSTER ABBEY, London (Eng.)

Enlarged 10 diameters (100 times area) from portion of miniature negative
developed with 'TABLOID' FINE-GRAIN DEVELOPER.

Enlargement equivalent to 30×20 in. from 3×2 in., or 15×10 in. from
$1\frac{1}{2} \times 1$ in. negative.

FLOODLIGHTS ON PHOTOGRAPHY

OF RECENT years the floodlights of science have illuminated the dim places in photography and dispelled for ever the need to grope in the dark. Processes previously obscure and complicated have become as clear as daylight, and even the gloomy depths of the dark room have been illuminated so that development can be carried out in a comfortable light.

It is now a simple matter to ensure a correctly-exposed and developed negative. There is no need for the antiquated method of trial and error, with its consequent waste of time and material, and often indifferent results.

Gone are the days when weights were essential; the only requirements for modern methods of preparing developing and other solutions are the requisite number of 'TABLOID' products, a measuring glass and a supply of water.

EXPOSURE

The beginner to-day can ensure success from every exposure at a small cost. He has simply to follow the system of photography explained in the 'WELLCOME' HANDBOOK AND DIARY.

It is a complete system, covering every aspect of photography, from the exposure to finished print or enlargement. It is a system specially devised to enable the amateur photographer to place his hobby on a sound scientific basis and get results which are comparable to those of the professional with the minimum expenditure of time and money. In a word, it makes photography *easy*.

This complete guide to successful photography eliminates guess-work. Written by practical photographers in simple non-technical language, it is easily understood by all. For the expert it provides tables and information unobtainable elsewhere.

Behind the 'WELLCOME' HANDBOOK AND DIARY is the Burroughs Wellcome & Co. staff of photographic experts. Registered users of the Handbook can obtain free the advice of these experts on any technical problem which may confront them.

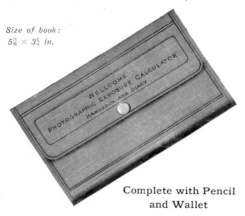

Size of book:
5⅜ × 3¼ in.

**Complete with Pencil
and Wallet**

This compact guide to photography contains the 'WELLCOME' EXPOSURE CALCULATOR, an ingenious invention, which shows by a disc, at a glance, the correct exposure for any subject. There are exposure factors and development times for every make of plate or film in regular use. These data are ascertained by independent tests in the Burroughs Wellcome & Co. Photographic Laboratories.

DEVELOPMENT

Although development by the perfect system of timing advocated and explained in detail in the 'Wellcome' Exposure Calculator, Handbook and Diary does away with the necessity of inspection during developing, many still find that one of the most fascinating features in photography is watching the gradual building up of the latent image created by the exposure.

To-day there is no need to develop in the gloomy depths of the dark room, as, by the use of 'TABLOID' DESENSITISER, development can be carried out in a comfortable light without risk of spoiling the fastest of plates or films.

A word about Developers

'TABLOID' BRAND DEVELOPERS offer definite advantages. They ensure the production of a developing solution of unvarying activity, readily prepared by the addition of the requisite volume of water. They remain active for years in any climate, and provide a range of agents which covers every development need.

For universal use, 'TABLOID' 'RYTOL' was originated by Burroughs Wellcome & Co. This provides a developer which is suitable for plates, films, bromide papers, gaslight papers, lantern slides and colour plates. It is the universal developer par excellence, and has been chosen for use by the official photographers of all the most important Expeditions of modern times. It produces soft, well-graded negatives admirably adapted for printing by artificial light or through the enlarger. Further, it does not stain the hands or negative and may be used with confidence by those susceptible to a metol developer.

'Tabloid'
'Rytol'
Developer

For those photographers who prefer a negative of the pyro type, 'TABLOID' 'TANCOL' will meet the most exacting requirements. This developer produces a negative slightly yellow in colour, giving good contrast and yielding bright, plucky prints. It is not suitable for use with bromide or gaslight papers.

'Tabloid'
'Tancol'
Developer

The latest addition to the list is 'TABLOID' FINE-GRAIN DEVELOPER, the result of prolonged research to discover a developer which would produce the minimum amount of grain in small negatives and so allow for the maximum amount of enlargement. From film negatives made with this developer, enlargements of 10 to 20 diameters (100 to 400 times the area) or more may be made without noticeable grain.

Fine-
Grain
Developer

Before   After

Print from negative before and after intensification with
TRADE MARK 'TABLOID' BRAND CHROMIUM INTENSIFIER

WESTMINSTER ABBEY, LONDON (ENG.)
Print developed with 'TABLOID' 'RYTOL' and toned with
'TABLOID' BLUE TONER

THE DUCKS

Negative and print developed with 'TABLOID' 'RYTOL,' bromide print toned with 'TABLOID' SEPIA TONER, 'TABLOID' BLUE and GREEN TONERS and stained with 'SOLOID' YELLOW STAIN

SUNLIT STREET IN MALTA

Developed with 'TABLOID' 'RYTOL'

Stained with 'SOLOID' YELLOW STAIN

INTENSIFICATION

Sometimes faulty negatives are caused by under-development or under-exposure. When this is the case, intensification will often considerably improve a negative.

The most satisfactory method of doing this is by the use of 'TABLOID' CHROMIUM INTENSIFIER. 'Tabloid' Chromium Intensifier With this Intensifier a slight or great degree of intensification may be obtained at will, with ease and certainty.

INEXPENSIVE COLOUR PHOTOGRAPHY

Have you ever considered making photographs in colour? This can be done either by adding colour to the ordinary black-and-white print, or by using a process that gives either prints or transparencies in natural colour.

The first method is by far the easier and is also less expensive. You can add the colour either by means of 'SOLOID' STAINS or by the use of 'TABLOID' TONERS. Prints in colour The difference is that a stain colours the whole print, while a toner leaves the white portions of the print untouched.

Either of these methods will be found to produce excellent results, and they provide a means of rendering a subject more in harmony with the predominating colour of the original scene than is often the case with a black-and-white reproduction.

In order to vary the results, you can use a combination of toners, or toners and stains, and, while this calls for a little practice, it is by no means difficult and opens up great opportunities for the display of individual expression.

Examples of the effects obtainable by the combined use of 'TABLOID' TONERS and 'SOLOID' STAINS are shown on the facing page. Full details of the method may be obtained on application to Burroughs Wellcome & Co. (U.S.A.) INC

_{TRADE MARK} 'TABLOID' BRAND

PHOTOGRAPHIC PRODUCTS

'Tabloid' Brand Developers

'TABLOID' 'RYTOL' UNIVERSAL DEVELOPER (25 of each)
,, ,, ,, ,, (100 of each)
'TABLOID' 'TANCOL' DEVELOPER
'TABLOID' FINE-GRAIN DEVELOPER
'TABLOID' AMIDOL DEVELOPER
'TABLOID' HYDROQUINONE (QUINOL) DEVELOPER
'TABLOID' METOL DEVELOPER
'TABLOID' METOL-QUINOL DEVELOPER
'TABLOID' PYRO-METOL DEVELOPER *(Imperial Standard Formula)*
'TABLOID' PYRO-SODA DEVELOPER *(Ilford Formula)*

'Tabloid' Brand Desensitiser

For Development without a dark-room

'TABLOID' DESENSITISER

'Tabloid' Brand Toners

For Bromide and Gaslight Prints or Lantern Slides

'TABLOID' BLUE TONER
'TABLOID' GREEN TONER
'TABLOID' SEPIA TONER
'TABLOID' BROWN TONER
'TABLOID' COPPER FERROCYANIDE TONING COMPOUND
'TABLOID' SULPHIDING COMPOUND

For P.O.P. Prints

'TABLOID' PLATINUM TONING COMPOUND
'TABLOID' GOLD CHLORIDE WITH SULPHOCYANIDE COMPOUND (B 6)
'TABLOID' GOLD CHLORIDE WITH THIOSULPHATE COMPOUND (COMBINED BATH) (B 10)

'Tabloid' Brand Restrainers

'TABLOID' AMMONIUM BROMIDE, gr. 1
'TABLOID' POTASSIUM BROMIDE, gr. 1
'TABLOID' SODIUM CITRATE, gr. 1

'Tabloid' Brand Sensitiser

'TABLOID' POTASSIUM AMMONIUM CHROMATE, gr. 24

'Tabloid' Brand Alkali

'TABLOID' SODIUM CARBONATE, gr. 44

'Tabloid' Brand Preservatives

'TABLOID' POTASSIUM METABISULPHITE, gr. 10
'TABLOID' SODIUM SULPHITE, DRIED, gr. 5

'Tabloid' Brand Hardener

'TABLOID' ALUM, gr. 10

'Tabloid' Brand Hardener and Clearer

'TABLOID' ALUM AND CITRIC ACID COMPOUND

'Tabloid' Brand Density Reducers

'TABLOID' AMMONIUM PERSULPHATE, gr. 11
'TABLOID' POTASSIUM FERRICYANIDE, gr. 2
'TABLOID' BLEACHING COMPOUND

'Tabloid' Brand Intensifiers

'TABLOID' CHROMIUM INTENSIFIER
'TABLOID' MERCURIC IODIDE AND SODIUM SULPHITE

'Tabloid' Brand Fixer

'TABLOID' SODIUM THIOSULPHATE (HYPO), DRIED, gr. 28·5

'Tabloid' Brand Products for Direct Colour Photography

'TABLOID' REVERSING COMPOUND
'TABLOID' COLOUR PLATE INTENSIFIER

TRADE MARK 'SOLOID' BRAND
PHOTOGRAPHIC STAINS

'SOLOID' PHOTO STAIN (GREEN)   For Colouring
'SOLOID' PHOTO STAIN (RED)   Bromide prints,
                                    Lantern slides,
'SOLOID' PHOTO STAIN (YELLOW)   etc.

'WELLCOME'
PHOTOGRAPHIC EXPOSURE CALCULATOR
HANDBOOK AND DIARY

Complete with pencil and Mechanical Exposure Calculator. U.S.A.
Edition *(in Red Cloth)*

Special Editions for Northern Hemisphere and Tropics; Southern Hemisphere and Tropics; and for Australasia and Tropics are also obtainable.

"'HAZELINE'
(Trade Mark)
SNOW''

Keeps the
skin cool, white
and smooth

'HAZELINE'
(Trade Mark)
CREAM

Used at
night
keeps the
skin right

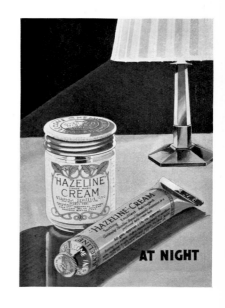

VALUABLE AIDS FOR
THE WOMAN BEAUTIFUL

"'HAZELINE' SNOW"
(Trade Mark)

Gives radiant beauty to the complexion—
for day and evening use.

'HAZELINE' CREAM
(Trade Mark)

Keeps the skin soft and supple.
For use at night.

'HAZELINE' SOAP
(Trade Mark)

Delightfully refreshing.

'WELLCOME' TOILET LANOLINE
(Trade Mark)

Keeps the hands smooth and beautiful.

Burroughs Wellcome & Co. products are obtainable of all Pharmacists and Druggists

FOR THE WOMAN BEAUTIFUL

AN ATTRACTIVE complexion and a smooth skin are assets of supreme value even to the "woman beautiful": many say no woman can be really beautiful without charm of complexion and a velvety skin.

Fortunately, neither expensive nor lengthy treatment is necessary. Simple methods are best and these can be carried out by the use of a few preparations which have an established reputation for exceptional purity.

TRADE "'HAZELINE' SNOW" MARK

"'HAZELINE' SNOW"—ideal for use during daytime and in
For day   preparation for evening functions. It keeps the skin
use   cool, white and smooth, protects it from the
influences of sun, sea and wind, and from the effects of overheated rooms.

"'HAZELINE' SNOW" is the best basis for toilet powder.

It is stimulating and comforting to the skin because it possesses the properties of 'Hazeline' *Hamamelis virginiana* distilled from fresh young twigs. It vanishes without trace of greasiness, leaving the skin comfortable and cool and giving the complexion a velvety bloom of great charm.

Collapsible tubes for the handbag and glass pots for home use ; also glass jars
containing 1 *lb.*

TRADE MARK 'HAZELINE' CREAM

'HAZELINE' CREAM is essentially a preparation for replacing the natural oil of the skin lost during the daytime as the result of subjecting the face, arms and neck to the drying effects of wind, sun, sea-water or alkaline soaps.

It combines 'Hazeline' with a basis closely resembling the
natural oil of the human skin and should be worked
For night   into the tired and dried-up tissues before retiring
use   for the night. Gently worked into the skin with
the fingers, it is absorbed to rejuvenate the tissues during the hours of rest.

Collapsible tubes of two sizes and glass pots: also glass jars containing 1 *lb.*

TRADE MARK 'HAZELINE' SOAP

A product which is used at least three times a day, or well over

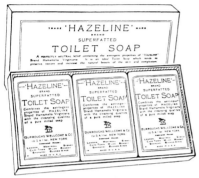

Reduced facsimile

a thousand times a year, as is soap, should be selected with special care. Toilet soaps vary considerably, many containing substances liable to coarsen the texture of the skin.

'HAZELINE' SOAP is one of the most delightful cleansers that science can provide or daintiness desire. Exceptionally pure and superfatted, it combines the astrin-

Pure super-fatted

gent properties of 'Hazeline' Brand *Hamamelis virginiana* with the detergent properties of a pure, milled soap. The excellent quality of 'HAZELINE' SOAP, and its freedom from excess of alkali, irritant substances and other impurities, make it particularly suited to the tender skin of infants.

Boxes containing three tablets

TRADE MARK 'WELLCOME' BRAND
TOILET LANOLINE

Reduced facsimile

Hands roughened or chapped by exposure to the winds, or reddened by strong sunshine, are quickly restored to their pristine beauty and softness by means of 'WELLCOME' TOILET LANOLINE.

'WELLCOME' TOILET LANOLINE makes good the wastage of the natural oils of the skin with a pure substance of closely similar constitution.

'WELLCOME' TOILET LANOLINE, applied immediately
before the hands are washed, obviates the coarsening
Soft, white   effects of hard water or unsuitable soaps, maintaining
hands   the white smoothness essential to beautiful hands.
The pleasing fragrance and creamy consistency of this high-class
preparation distinguish it from ordinary lanolines of commerce.

'WELLCOME' TOILET LANOLINE is one of the most
universally valued of dressing-table necessities.

Collapsible tubes of two sizes and glass jars containing 1 *lb.*

TO INCREASE THE PLEASURE
OF LEISURE HOURS

ON regular vacation, or on short holidays spent in the open
air, there is need to provide against causes which may hinder full
enjoyment of the leisure which is all too short and infrequent.

For example, the pleasures of bathing and the subsequent
sunbath may be ruined by scorching, irritation or other skin
discomfort.

TRADE MARK 'C A R O F A X' BRAND

SOLIDIFIED CARRON OIL *(with* 2 *per cent. of Phenol)*

'CAROFAX' protects sensitive skins. By a timely application,
sunburn can be avoided and healthy sun-tan encouraged. When
no method of protection against the scorching rays
Protects and   of the sun has been adopted, at the first sign of
soothing   redness apply 'CAROFAX.' It will soothe the
smarting skin and prevent blistering.

'CAROFAX' is a preparation of creamy consistency. It is
pleasant to use and easily and quickly applied. A tube can be
carried in the handbag or pocket.

'CAROFAX' is also useful as a first-aid application
(see page 127*)*.

Collapsible tubes of three sizes and glass jars containing 16 *ounces*

TRADE MARK 'SKETOFAX' BRAND
AROMATIC CREAM

The mosquito can be anything from an intolerable nuisance to a deadly menace. Residents, workers or picnickers in any place infested with mosquitoes will find in 'SKETOFAX' a valuable means of protection. Gnats, midges and sand-flies, if less dangerous than mosquitoes, are equally objectionable. 'SKETOFAX' acts as a deterrent against these insects. It is a pleasant, aromatic, non-staining cream, and should be applied *lightly* to exposed parts of the body.

Deters mosquitoes, etc.

'SKETOFAX' is a boon to the angler, automobilist, golfer, tennis player, river enthusiast, and to all lovers of the open air.

It is a necessity in malarial districts.

'SKETOFAX' gives protection to the prudent and is a soothing application to those who have been bitten.

'SKETOFAX' is convenient to carry and pleasant to use.

Collapsible tubes

TRADE MARK 'TABLOID' BRAND TEA

A Cup of Delicious Tea Made in a Moment

Reduced facsimile

When time is short, an easily-made cup of refreshing tea is a great boon. One to two products of 'TABLOID' TEA in each cup, boiling water, milk and sugar to taste—and the tea is ready.

For picnic and holiday use, 'TABLOID' TEA is ideal.

First thing in the morning, at breakfast, in mid-afternoon or at odd times, the time-saving, labour-saving qualities of 'TABLOID' TEA are much appreciated.

Specially selected for its delicious aroma, 'TABLOID' TEA has been freed from tannin-containing portions such as the midrib and stalk. The result is a compressed leaf which is more economical than ordinary loose teas. Moreover, the strength of the infusion can always be gauged accurately, because 'Tabloid' products are constant in weight.

Constant strength and quality

'TABLOID' TEA, carefully wrapped in tinfoil and packed in a neat, hinged-lid tin, undergoes no loss of strength on keeping. The tea made from the last product of the tin is as delicious as that prepared from the first.

'TABLOID' TEA *(Special Blend)*—a unique blend of the choicest varieties—is also available.

Hinged-lid tins of 100 and 200 ; Special Blend, hinged-lid tins of 100

TRADE MARK 'TABLOID' BRAND 'SAXIN' TRADE MARK

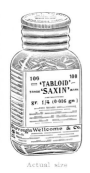

Actual size

A delicious sweetening agent without food value.

A great convenience for campers, hikers, sportsmen and picnickers. Each tiny product is equal in sweetening power to one large lump, two small lumps, or one teaspoonful of sugar. Its compactness enables it to be carried in the pocket or handbag.

Bottles of 100, 200 *and* 500

Burroughs Wellcome & Co. products are obtainable of all Pharmacists and Druggists

Burroughs Wellcome & Co.
Offices, Warehouses and Works

IN THE UNITED STATES OF AMERICA, CANADA,
ENGLAND, ITALY, AUSTRALIA, SOUTH AFRICA, INDIA
AND CHINA

THE WELLCOME CHEMICAL AND GALENICAL WORKS
AND EXPERIMENTAL RESEARCH LABORATORIES
NEW YORK, U.S.A.

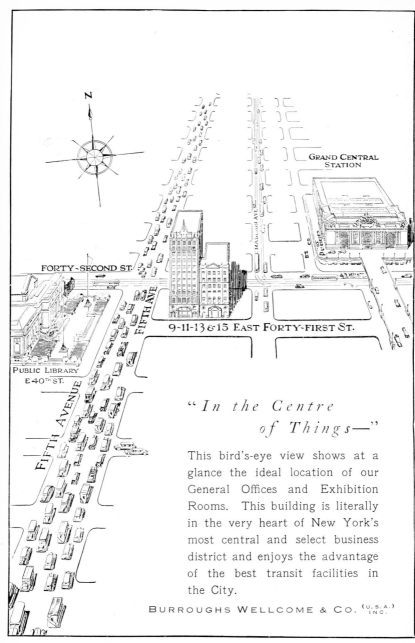

N

GRAND CENTRAL
STATION

FORTY~SECOND ST.

FIFTH AVE

9-11-13 &15 EAST FORTY-FIRST ST.

PUBLIC LIBRARY
E 40TH ST.

FIFTH AVENUE

"*In the Centre of Things*—"

This bird's-eye view shows at a
glance the ideal location of our
General Offices and Exhibition
Rooms. This building is literally
in the very heart of New York's
most central and select business
district and enjoys the advantage
of the best transit facilities in
the City.

BURROUGHS WELLCOME & CO. (U.S.A.) (INC.)

ZONE MAP

BURROUGHS WELLCOME & CO. (U.S.A.) (INC.)
GENERAL OFFICES AND EXHIBITION ROOMS
9–11 & 13–15, East Forty-first Street, NEW YORK CITY

The Wellcome Chemical and Galenical Works and Experimental Research Laboratories
New York, U.S.A.

BURROUGHS
WELLCOME & CO.

OFFICES
AND
EXHIBITION
ROOMS

1105, SHERBROOKE STREET
WEST
(CORNER OF PEEL STREET)
MONTREAL

K

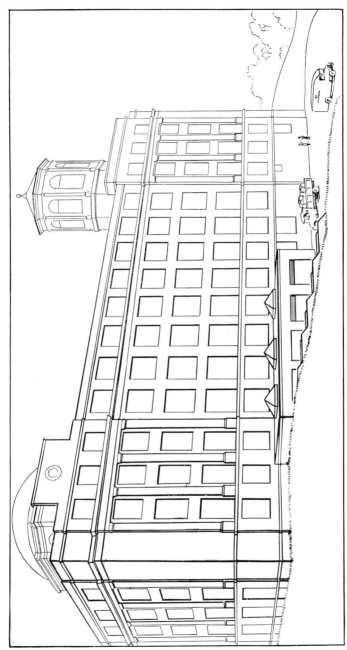

The Wellcome Chemical and Galenical Works and Laboratories
Montreal, Canada

BURROUGHS WELLCOME & CO., LONDON
(THE WELLCOME FOUNDATION LTD.)

Chief Offices:
SNOW HILL BUILDINGS, LONDON, E.C.1 (ENG.)

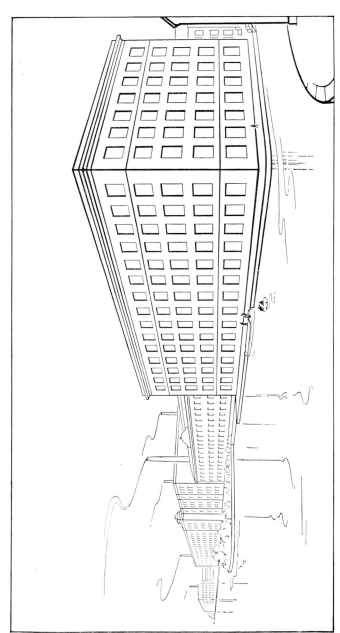

Section of the Wellcome Chemical and Galenical Works and Laboratories
Dartford, Kent, England

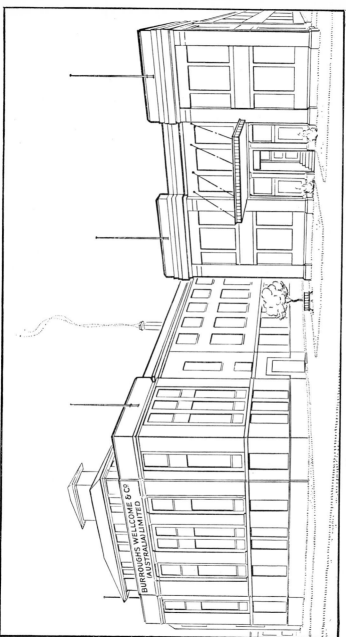

BURROUGHS WELLCOME & CO. (AUSTRALIA) LTD.

Offices and Works: SYDNEY, N.S.W.

BURROUGHS WELLCOME & CO.
OFFICES, WAREHOUSES AND WORKS

NEW YORK*

NEW YORK

MONTREAL

SYDNEY

MONTREAL†

* Wellcome Chemical and Galenical Works and Experimental Research Laboratories
New York

† Wellcome Chemical and Galenical Works and Laboratories
Ville LaSalle, near Montreal, Canada

BURROUGHS WELLCOME & CO.
OFFICES, WAREHOUSES AND WORKS

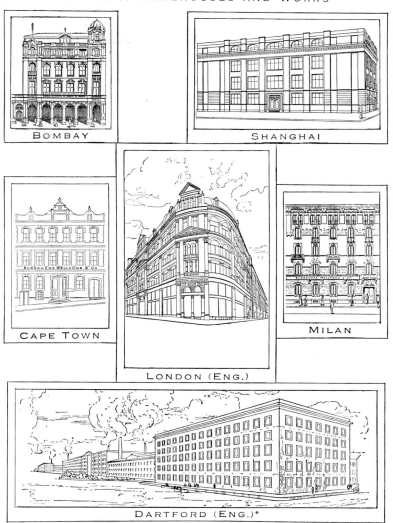

BOMBAY

SHANGHAI

CAPE TOWN

LONDON (ENG.)

MILAN

DARTFORD (ENG.)*

* Section of the Wellcome Chemical and Galenical Works
Dartford, Kent, England

LIÉGE
SIX
GRAND PRIZES

THREE
DIPLOMAS OF
HONOUR

THREE
GOLD MEDALS

ST. LOUIS
THREE
GRAND PRIZES
THREE
GOLD MEDALS
SEATTLE
(Alaska-Yukon-Pacific)
ONE GRAND
PRIZE

MILAN
THREE
GRAND PRIZES

THREE
DIPLOMAS OF
HONOUR

ONE
GOLD MEDAL

LONDON
(Franco-British)
SEVEN
GRAND PRIZES
ONE
DIPLOMA OF
HONOUR
TWO
GOLD MEDALS

LONDON
(Japan-British)

FIVE
GRAND PRIZES

ONE
GOLD MEDAL

LONDON
(Festival of Empire)

TWO
GRAND PRIZES

ONE
GOLD MEDAL

LONDON
(International
Congress of Medicine)

TWO
GRAND PRIZES

BUENOS AIRES
ONE
GRAND PRIZE

ALLAHABAD
ONE
GOLD MEDAL

BRUSSELS
EIGHT
GRAND PRIZES

THREE
DIPLOMAS OF
HONOUR
ONE
GOLD MEDAL

At every great
INTERNATIONAL
EXHIBITION
at which the
BURROUGHS
WELLCOME & CO.
products have been
exhibited they have
received the greatest
number of
COMPETITIVE
HIGHEST AWARDS
These now exceed
270

TURIN
EIGHT
GRAND PRIZES

TWO
DIPLOMAS OF
HONOUR

THREE
GOLD MEDALS

INDEX

Figures in heavy type throughout this Index refer to Illustrations

'TABLOID'

The word 'TABLOID' is a registered Trade Mark.

The word 'TABLOID' denotes a Burroughs Wellcome & Co. product and is applied to many classes of products.

The word 'TABLOID' on a package, wherever purchased, ensures supreme and uniform quality.

The word 'TABLOID' may not be used except with reference to a Burroughs Wellcome & Co. product.

BEWARE OF IMITATIONS

'TABLOID' was registered as a Trade Mark in 1884, over 50 years ago